From a Coastal Schooner's Log

From a Coastal Schooner's Log

Claude K. Darrach

Illustrations by L. B. Jenson

Nova Scotia Museum
Halifax, N.S.
1979

Published by
The Nova Scotia Museum
as a part of
The Education Resource Services Program
of the
DEPARTMENT OF EDUCATION
Province of Nova Scotia

Hon. Terence R. B. Donahoe
Minister

Carmen F. Moir
Deputy Minister

Produced by the Nova Scotia
Communications & Information Centre

Printed in Canada

ISBN 0-919680-10-0
© Nova Scotia Museum 1979

Contents

Foreword

With the disappearance of commercial sailing craft — the square rigged ships and fore-and-aft schooners — a real effort is being made, by those with first hand knowledge and experience, to record the characteristics of design and construction of these vessels. Today, when the beauty of the sailing ship is seen no more and seamanship is becoming a lost art, it is equally important that a description of the men who sailed them be recorded and preserved, as a part of our maritime history.

It is hoped that *From a Coastal Schooner's Log* will tell the story of the Nova Scotia trading schooners during the latter part of the last century and the early years of the present one, and illustrate their contribution to the economic life of the province. It will also, we hope, tell the reader something of the type of men who sailed them.

Their way of life, both at sea and in port, is described in the story of two rival captains, who in this case are fictitious. However, their daily lives are re-created from first hand experience, and although told as fiction, would be typical of the many men sailing in the coastal trade at that time.

I trust that this will serve as a fitting tribute to the men and schooners of the coastal trading era.

Claude K. Darrach, M.B.E.
Herring Cove, Nova Scotia

Introduction

Competition was keen among the trading schooners operating along the coast of the Maritime Provinces during the latter half of the 1800's and up to the beginning of World War I, in 1914. Thrift, intelligence, seamanship and courage were required on the part of those involved. Also, the success of any venture depended largely on the cunningness of each captain, who in nearly every case was owner, master, supercargo and general manager of the business.

Agents had not been thought of by the captains of these coastal vessels, in the sense that there were recognized representatives of any particular vessels or master, however, a shrewd and thrifty master was quite capable of taking stock of the natives living in the many bays, inlets and ports where his vessel called to trade. After sizing up the situation, he would pick out some person or persons outstanding in the community and work in cooperation with them, making use of their influence in that locality. He would thus have a local person with whom to deal when doing business in that port of call.

The wood-constructed vessels, sometimes called coastal packets, operated for approximately ten months of each year, laying up for the two winter months of January and February for refit and overhaul.

The cabin of these little schooners was located in the stern section and was entered through a companionway immediately in front of the steering wheel. After descending a seven foot step ladder, you found yourself in a cabin averaging about seventeen feet wide by twelve feet long. Two spacious bunks on each side were snugly located under the main deck, and could be entered through an opening three feet high by four and one-half feet long, cut out of the beautiful light oak panelled cabin walls which were highly varnished and without stain. A square cabin house (trunk style), built up from the main deck for about thirty inches immediately over the cabin, also had a very well finished deckhead. Very narrow groove and tongue pine was used as finish over the large eight by six inch deck beams. This deckhead, painted with gloss white paint and having a glass skylight in the centre, made attractive and normally well-lighted surroundings.

In the centre of the cabin floor stood a round bellied cast iron stove with a front door through which a bucket of hard coal could easily be dumped. The stove was very securely lashed with wire stays and was commonly called the "bogey".

Out in the extreme stern sections, known as the overhang, and accessible from the cabin, was a considerable amount of storage space very suitable for small package cargo. Except for the very rare occasion when a passenger (and one whom the master would rate as wardroom rank) was making a trip, the captain was the sole occupant of the cabin. This was a convenient arrangement for privacy when discussing business or entertaining friends on board. Therefore it was common to see a few coils of new manila rope lying about the cabin floor, or the spare bunks cluttered with small package goods, and a bundle of canvas stored in the corner or against the bulkhead. A flat-top oak desk table with a couple of drawers on one side provided the main office and filing cabinet, the top drawer being fitted with a good quality inset lock. This, then, is to be remembered as the captain's private quarters and business office.

No crafty skipper ever sailed on a trading voyage without ample supply of good old Demerara rum and pipe tobacco, solely for entertaining purposes. For the rum, half-gallon stone jugs were the popular containers; for the tobacco plugs, wooden boxes of five pounds each. Had bookkeeping been a detailed affair, probably entertaining might have been charged up to advertising and agent's services.

These schooners provided the lifeline of supplies to the outports and were the chief means of transporting their requirements and produce for market and export.

To illustrate and describe more fully the actual life aboard and the operation of these vessels, this story will deal with a supposed pair of the keenest, most competitive, rival skippers of the fleet. The names of the schooners and the names of persons are fictitious and are simply chosen for the purpose of making up the rank and file required. The routes taken, and the distances given, are fairly accurate. The meanderings ashore are pretty much as they actually were, and so is the dry sense of humor common among the people of these rural coastal communities of that time.

Rival Skippers

Captain Abraham Young in the schooner *Western Belle* and Captain Moses Griffin in the trim little schooner *Lucy B.* were two of the most popular and successful operators on the coast. The *Western Belle*, 54 tons (net tonnage) was built in western Nova Scotia for the North Bay cod fishery but was not the best design for that purpose. She was designed with very bluff bows and heavy, full stern sections — not a good Bank fisherman, but an excellent cargo carrier, with reasonably shallow draft. Only an average sailer, she proved later to be a very good coastal trading vessel. Her captain and owner was a rugged six-foot, two hundred and eighteen pound, raring-to-go, windjammer skipper.

The *Lucy B.* was also built in Nova Scotia and was a trim-looking vessel. She was a very good sailer, and worked exceptionally well when tacking in and out of narrow channels and harbors. The *Lucy B.'s* captain was a much smaller, sandy-complexioned man, with a heavy moustache, who had that ability to choose and buy clothes that matched, which gave him a neat, tidy, gentlemanly appearance.

The port of Halifax, capital of Nova Scotia, was the supply base. Here the two-mile-long waterfront shipping section was forever adorned with a forest of tall, graceful masts and yards of the finest foreign-going sailing ships of all nations — the finest and best from the Far East, Australia, India, Egypt and Africa — with tea, spices, rice, dried fruit, hemp and manila, cutch, mahogany, teak, lignum vitae, and the many essentials used by the variety of labor and industry along our coast. From Spain, France, Scandinavian and United Kingdom ports came the full-rigged ships. The British West Indies trade was well taken care of by smaller vessels such as barquentines, brigantines and schooners. The ships from Spain, Portugal and France brought dried fruits, wines, fisheries, salt and tobacco. From the United Kingdom came cutlery, ship building equipment, high-class furniture, the famous Scotch and Irish whiskeys, special, blended tobacco, machinery, coal, linen and clay

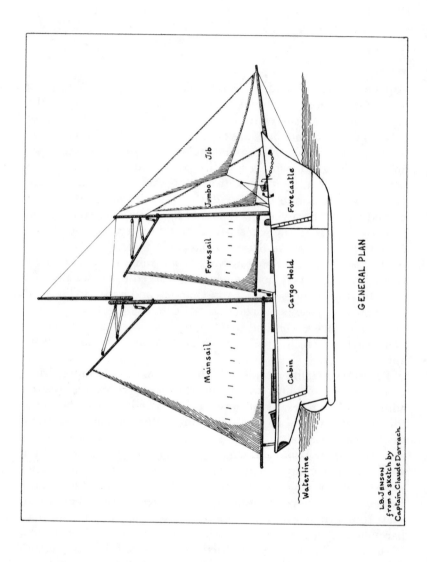

Jib

Jumbo

Forecastle

Foresail

Cargo Hold

Mainsail

Cabin

Waterline

GENERAL PLAN

L.B. Jenson
from a sketch by
Captain Claude Darrach.

bricks. Scandinavian ships usually brought the export of the South American countries and carried away cargoes of wheat and lumber for their home ports.

Skipper Moses' *Lucy B.* and Abe's *Western Belle* never rated in that class, but in their own small way played the part of distributing a portion of each and every item mentioned to the outports of the Maritime Provinces with the occasional voyage to Newfoundland and the French isle of St. Pierre, off the south coast of Newfoundland. Having to rely entirely on sail to make a voyage, their schedule was figured out and maintained only on what wind and weather provided. Calm weather, with fog, kept them practically motionless as far as sailing from one port to the other was concerned, so it was "take what you get" from whatever opportunities the weather had to offer.

Any captain being the owner of a staunch and seaworthy vessel, and having established credit with most of the many merchants of Halifax and the outports, was in a position to engage in the arts and angles of peddling foodstuffs, merchandise, fishing gear, and all other necessities of life, but seldom received actual cash settlements. Merchandise in exchange for local products was generally the rule; or else an agreement to accept and transport the various products to market and bring back the money to the producer on the return voyage. In some cases, small firms operating in many of the ports did the buying and selling and made use of the coasting vessel for transportation purposes only.

Wednesday, the second day of March, was a fine, clear, sunny spring day on the eastern coast of Nova Scotia. Captain Abe Young, being a sou'western shore Young, had the *Western Belle* registered at Halifax. (To seafaring people of Nova Scotia, west of Halifax people are Sou'Western Shore men, and east of Halifax, Eastern Shore men.) For the months of January and February he kept the vessel in one of the snug inlets of Mahone Bay where the rigging, hull and sails were overhauled and put in shape for the next season. In this part of Nova Scotia where usually no ice formed in the harbors, vessels could come and go as they desired. Therefore, Abe had completed all repairs on *Western Belle* and was in Halifax taking on cargo the last week in February, and when Customs opened that fine March morning, Skipper Abraham Young was one of the first at the Clearance Clerk's wicket to apply for permission to sail on the first trading voyage of the season.

From Halifax eastward to St. Peters, Cape Breton Isle, there were roughly thirty-six ports of call before turning for Halifax to discharge cargo that had been picked up, and to replenish a load for the eastern route again.

Of all the many trading schooners operating, the *Western Belle* and *Lucy B.* were the two most popular and enterprising. Both skippers highly respected each other, but by the same token were rivals in business, in no uncertain terms.

"Good morning!" Captain Young greeted the familiar bearded face behind the Customs House wicket.

"Looks like an early start for the season, or is spring really here and I don't recognize it?"

"What can I do for you, Captain?"

"Why, get me fixed up with me clearance for the *Western Belle* down the Eastern Shore so far as Country Harbor, loaded with 80 tons general cargo."

"That's fine, Captain. I see by yesterday's ice reports all Eastern Shore harbors are free of ice right down to White Head and the schooners down that way are beginning to move already."

"They is, hey? Yes, I 'spose! Any reports of the Country Harbor fleet moving yet, sir?"

The officer walked down a long desk, ran through a file, and rushed back.

"Yes, Captain Young, the *Nannie O'Hara, Maud G.* and *Lucy B.* sailed for Halifax Monday evening."

"Is that so? Sailed Monday did they? Ye better be giving me them papers, Officer. I better not be delayed in here any longer."

"Yes, Captain — vessel's tonnage, please?"

"Fifty-four net," was the answer.

"You've seen the shipping master and signed on the crew? Could I see the crew list, and take a glance at the manifest, Captain, please?"

Captain Young had the necessary bundle of documents already at hand and passed them through the wicket without delay: Bill Publicover, mate; Reuben Zinck, deck hand; Caleb Madera, deck hand; Millwood Jack, cook.

Laying down the crew list and looking over the manifest, the officer soon learned the items of general cargo — hay, bran, manila rope, molasses, flour, nails, tea, condensed milk, salt, lumber and salt beef. He carefully folded the manifest and crew list, brought forward a handful of papers he had been preparing for the King's Stamp, and looked through the wicket, saying:

4

"All is correct, Captain. It will only be port dues and lighthouse fees and come this way, please, away down the other end of the longroom."

Clump, clump, clump went the heavy stamp, and in less than two minutes Captain Young was handed a brand new, hard, brown, folding envelope neatly tied with tape and stamped "Official Papers — Schooner *Western Belle.*"

The next big move for Captain Abraham was to get the *Western Belle* away from the pier before the other vessels arrived. He was first loaded, and in a good position to get contacts with the best fishermen and merchants along the coast, providing he was capable of avoiding any trap he might accidentally fall into, with three rival skippers about to close in on him at any time. Just around the corner, and not far from the Customs, was Pat Ryan's bar-room, just two zigs and a zag off the direct course from the Customs House and Boake and Bennet's Wharf where the *Western Belle* was berthed, bow out. Abe made the two zigs and a long zag and brought up at the bar.

"A double rum straight, 'Chips', and wrap a couple of pints of good brandy and a long neck o' Demerara."

Abe took a careful glance at the customers, most of whom were crew members from bank-fishing vessels in off the Sable Island banks. Seeing no one he recognized as crew members of the trading schooners, he took departure for Boake and Bennet's Wharf, to get underway.

Mate Publicover knew the business of coastal trading as well as he knew the weather, and when Abe turned down the long narrow pier head, he was happy to see the *Western Belle* moored close to the end of the jetty with the main and foresail hoisted, all ready for slipping off on the voyage. Abe didn't figure it good policy to show any appreciation for the mate's helpful move and good judgement, but addressed the cook instead, saying:

"Lucky I made it in time, Cook, looks like you fellows don't mind sailing short-handed."

Altering his glance a couple of points back aft,

"How about it, Mate, can we have time for a quick one before we let go?"

"About time somebody said that aboard here — she's that dry, the capstan's creaking," came back the mate.

"Oh, that's bad," said Abe, "somebody should have mentioned it before."

5

By this time, all hands were climbing down the forecastle and when Abe's keen eye sighted the sugar can on the cook's work-locker, and a scattered white mug here and there, he was sure he had missed the first hot toddy of the day. However, he gave no hint of what he well knew had been taking place while he was ashore, and only announced, while he opened the parcel to get a bottle out, that it was "too bad about that capstan creaking so bad."

After a quick hot toddy all round, *plunk* went the cork in the bottle and, at the same time, Abe said:

"All right now, what are we waiting for? Away we go."

He purposely placed himself in the mate's way to delay him while the others climbed the ladder and on deck, but only for sufficient time and privacy to pass the mate a pint of brandy with the suggestion that he "pay better attention to the capstan."

With the sails already hoisted, the schooner began to get restless. It's not for a seasoned old schooner to have mooring lines holding her fast. She was performing that uneasy motion of lurching ahead on the lines and rubbing hard against the jetty pilings, making them groan. Soon the groan would be replaced by a rhythmic rippling sound made by the sea-water as her bow passed gracefully through.

It was just a matter of minutes when Captain Abe came up from his cabin, his shore-going togs left below, and wearing a heavy, turtleneck sweater and tight-fitting blue bib melton cap.

"All right, forward; slip them bow-lines."

Abe walked over to the mooring-bit, near the steering wheel, to where the stern-line was made fast, flipped the turns off the bit-post and, in a few seconds, had manoeuvered a snake twirl in the four-inch circumference manila rope; the large eye that circled the jetty mooring-post made a vertical take-off and climbed up over the top of the post to set the old schooner free.

"Trim that fore-sheet in and hoist the jumbo and jib."

While this was going on, Captain Abe was throwing his two hundred and eighteen pounds and muscle in on the main-sheet. The light breeze was from the north and when the *Western Belle's* sails filled, the wind carried them over on the starboard side and she picked up headway. She headed in an easterly direction, and had only one hundred yards to go to reach the main shipping channel in which she could be steered southerly for a distance of seven and one-half miles to the automatic fairway buoy, and on into the broad Atlantic Ocean.

Several sails were sighted — some ships departing for ocean crossings and others coming up over the horizon inbound with cargoes from foreign ports. The *Western Belle,* choosing a route along the Eastern Shore of Nova Scotia, was not required to sail all the way out to the fairway buoy and could save time by rounding Thrum Cap Shoals, passing close off the Devil's Island. She steered an E by S course, to pass well off the Shut-in Island Shoals and on to Jeddore Rock, a bluff rock with a lighthouse at the entrance to Jeddore Harbor — a large, navigable harbor where quite a number of people lived, working in the woods, and fishing for a living. From wharf to wharf, Halifax to Jeddore, is an estimated distance of thirty-eight miles. After passing outward beyond George's Island, Skipper Abe sized up the weather situation and reckoned he could depend on a breeze sufficient to make an average seven knots all day, and on that basis could very well be berthed at the Government Wharf at Rum Point in Jeddore Harbor before nightfall.

It was 20 minutes before noon when both range lights on Devil's Island came in line and the *Western Belle* altered course from southerly to E by S, her sheets trimmed on all four lowers, and settled down on the voyage for Jeddore Rock and the entrance to the Harbor. As her bows steadied up on the E by S course, and the wind filled the sails on a broad angle, the old vessel heeled over to ten degrees, bringing the strain on all the port-side shrouds and rigging. There was that old sound familiar to all windjammer sailor-men: the creaking, stretching and stressing sounds made by wire rigging, and hemp and manila ropes, as each gives and takes, to even up and share the load they must carry. As the ship lurches and heaves in the seaway, that stress constantly moves from one shroud and rope to another, back and forth, in such a fashion that the drone and creak harmonizes and blends in time with the motion of the waves; and even though you may be sound asleep in a bunk below decks, you relax to that free and easy sensation that only a sailing ship can offer. And this was true on the *Western Belle,* at that moment.

Jack, the cook, was placing the dishes on the forecastle table and the aroma of spareribs and sauerkraut scented the air about the companionway and out through the ventilation scuttle. Once in a while the crest of a wave gurgled in through the lee scuppers, and washed the coal-dust and sand accumulation from the crevices of the bulwark stanchions, bringing back the salty look that all

7

seagoing vessels acquire when in operation. All this time, while Abe steered the vessel on her course, he would occasionally hear more than the usual loud conversation coming from below — a burst of laughter after a long silence, and so on. All this gave him good reason to believe that the odd hot toddy could still be the special attraction below decks. He was confirmed in his belief when the mate tripped over the grub-beam and bit the stem clean off a brand-new white clay pipe, on the way aft to relieve the skipper for dinner. Abe got a good laugh and took the opportunity to mention that in his opinion, it was not only the capstan that was well-oiled now. Bill's two big problems at that moment were to brace himself on deck, and to spit out the broken fragments of clay pipe stem.

"This all looks like the proper way to start a season," Abe observed, "and I think I can do with an appetizer myself. Well, Mate, she's all yours now," he said, and with a grin and a quick takeoff, "if yer vision is not too heavy oiled, east by south by the compass."

"East to south by the compass, old man," came the reply.

About this time, an estimated fifty miles down the coast, where the wind blew a stiff 20 knots from the northeast, was a picture any marine artist would rate as the one in a million. Just about two and one-half miles off Beaver Island, and within a range of less than one half mile of each other, were three schooners, lee rails awash, under four lowers, and heading for Halifax, logging off an average of eight and one half knots. In the lead was the *Nannie O'Hara*, second the *Maude G.* and, gradually closing the gap, the trim and above average sailer, *Lucy B.* There was every reason to wager a safe bet that the *Lucy B.* would overtake both vessels and be first to arrive in Halifax, but with every square yard of canvas pulling its best and the broad, white, foaming bow-wave glistening in the western sun, the three little windjammers made a picture, alive and thrilling, which displayed the combination of effort in every strand of rope and every foot of schooner, as the wheelsmen kept them on their courses. The next three hours saw the *Lucy B.* move along to take approximately a one mile lead over the *O'Hara* and *Maud G.* and she was coming through the channel between Egg Island and Long Island on a west nor'westerly course for the entrance to Halifax Harbor, approximately thirty-four miles away.

Life on board the *Western Belle* for the past three hours had been pretty uneventful. Abe had "eaten hearty" of the spareribs and sauerkraut and was in the bunk, in sockfeet and shirt-clad, snoring a breeze, when Caleb Madera came down and woke him up.

"Wind's backed to nor'east, old man, and she falls a bit to loo'ard her course, and three vessels east of Jeddore Rock heading wester'd."

"Where we at now, Madera?" yawned Abe.

"A mile and a bit loo'ard Musquodoboit Shoals, and she wants to head off east south east."

Captain Abe, pulling on the heavy turtle-neck sweater, and high leather boots (better known to Bluenose seamen as "Red Jacks"), climbed on deck and made a quick survey of the eastern horizon.

"That's them, 'tis the pirate fleet of the coasting trade, that's the *Lucy B.* ahead with me mutual friend, Skipper Mose. I'll take the wheel now, Zinck, we got to tack ship soon, and get close and hail Mose. See how he stood up the last couple months."

Within an hour, the two schooners were being manoeuvred in such a manner that the wind would be spilled out of the sails and they would jog side by side long enough for a brief conversation. This was done by the *Western Belle* being brought about on the starboard tack, in a position and angle where the schooner was now heading in a NNW direction. With the head sails sheeted back to windward, the rudder fixed on an angle intended to turn the vessel in a clockwise circle but with the main and fore sheets trimmed slack, the ship could not gather headway enough to carry on around on the circular track, but rather remained zigging and zagging and getting nowhere.

In this manner, Captain Mose's move was to keep the *Lucy B.* directly, and about two hundred yards, astern of the *Western Belle,* and then shoot the *Lucy* right up in the wind's eye, which would bring her only a few feet away. By the time she had travelled that distance, she would have also come practically to a stop. The schooners would then remain in a hailing distance for possibly five minutes.

Captain Mose, having to be the more concerned on the conning of the *Lucy* at this stage of the hailing manoeuver, gave Abe the first chance to come up with the greeting.

"Ahoy there, young feller," shouted Abe, "Why yer fatter 'an a young pup. Ye been eatin' too much wild ducks and moose meat."

"Howdy, Captain Abe, good to see you again. You don' look too bad yourself, fer an old man."

Mose knew for sure he had to counteract that "old man" remark without further delay, and carried right on: "You got a fine lot of freight in that vessel, Captain, she looks good."

"This old man and schooner always looks good, and what have you got in that barnacle-chawed hulk of yours? She looks to be well down in the water."

"The hold's full of green, chopped hardwood, Abraham! Makes good ballast and sells good, nowadays. Fish plants wants all they can get, for smoke-house use. Where you making the first call, Captain?"

"Why, Jeddore, and tonight for sure. No freight for there, just going to take in a square dance, and pie social."

By this time both schooners had jogged too far apart to continue any further conversation, so the operation of getting *Western Belle* on her feet again was begun. The two head sails that were sheeted across to windward were slacked away and trimmed on the lee (port) side; the rudder fixed on an angle of thirty degrees off the line of the keel and to starboard (windward). The schooner being just about "in irons", now would start to move astern. Following the rudder angle, the bow of the ship would fall to port and bring the wind in over the starboard side. Then, immediately on trimming in the main and foresail sheets, and bringing the rudder to midships (in line with the keel), the schooner would pick up headway and be off again.

Heading in on that tack had to be short, because the Musquodoboit Shoals lay to windward, only a short distance now. So, after a short tack and about on the SE course again, the *Nannie O'Hara* passed along about one quarter of a mile away. The greeting between the two schooners was a waving of caps exchanged among all crew members on the deck of each schooner. The *Maud G.*, a smaller schooner than the others, trailed behind, but as proud and colorful as any of them, and exhibiting as far as one could see, a deck-load of barreled fish.

At five p.m. the *Western Belle* came about on the starboard tack to clear Brig Shoal and head in on a N by W course for four and one-half miles to Thorn Shoal buoy and the entrance to the narrow channel leading into the shelter and harbor of Jeddore.

All this was accomplished by seven p.m. and when Captain Abe hauled into the supper table, the first announcement was,

"Did you fellers hear gentleman Mose call me an old man today? Pity the heat in Halifax wouldn't run the maple sap out o' that green hardwood and clog his bilges and pump-pipes with sugar. I always figgered them smoke-houses was run with sawdust."

Millwood Jack, who was a sort of fleet-footed breed from an inland settlement, made the first comment on this subject and made known that the fires were made from dry hardwood and smothered with sawdust.

The news that a trading schooner had arrived in Jeddore and was berthed at the Government Jetty, at Rum Point, soon travelled the grapevine communication system and by ten p.m. that night the oil lamp that swung in a set of gimbals from the cabin and cargo hold bulkhead was just about visible in pipe smoke. Some people had arrived by ox teams and others had crossed the Bay in row-boats. Two local merchants, Mr. Ronald and Mr. Folkman, asked for morning deliveries of hay, bran, corn and some salt beef. Several coils of lobster rope went to the fishermen that night. Captain Abe had several invitations to visit ashore but made no commitments on the spur of the moment. There were places to go in any of these small ports, but well Abe knew he had to make hay while the sun shone, and attend to his business.

After the evening's visitors had left and the cabin was cleared, the captain was working on his crude ledger, balancing the sales against the cargo, etc., when Jack, the cook, shouted down the companionway:

"Ahoy, Skipper! Ain't ye comin' out a that smoke-infected kennel for some fresh air and a mug up, before turning in fer the night?"

Abe knew in a split second that this was an "invite" to the forecastle for something special. Cooks don't usually bother much if the skipper smothers in pipe-smoke or gets fresh air, and Abe took the hint the first kick-off.

"Good idea, Cook, got some hot tea left down there? Anyway, come down fer a minute."

The cook had reckoned it might work out that way and lost no time fleet-footing down the cabin companionway.

"Take a sound of that jug, Cook, see what's left."

It was a half-gallon earthenware jug, sitting in a coil of rope up against the bulkhead.

"The way them people stuck to that jug you'd a thought it was Christmas. Did they leave you a drink?"

"Yes, too much, old man, ye have to split with me."

"Ye mean it's that dry, Cook?"

"Now, 'tis, old man, but here, ye got a good snort left," and as

11

Abe heard the cook make the second long swallow, he knew who got the best of the split, and as they walked forward along the deck, Abe appreciated the cool, clear night atmosphere.

When he seated himself at the table, Jack presented a large plateful of fried eels, baked potatoes and a fourteen-ounce mug of hot tea — special schooner brew — tea with the sugar and condensed milk supplied to the teapot before pouring.

"I never knew you was so good at spearing eels, Cook. Must of knew just where to go."

"No, Skipper, we no spear them eels. Old Mr. Jimmerix' boys brought 'em. I usually finds a mug-up for the young lads, and they once in a while comes up with a few eels, or maybe a kettle of blueberries. I reckon we breaks even for the season."

"Well, keep playin' 'em on, Cook, I got no complaints on a feed like this."

While all this was going on board *Western Belle*, Captain Mose of the *Lucy B.* was doing the rounds in Halifax, visiting relatives and renewing old acquaintances. Having arrived too late that evening for any business, the *Lucy B.* was berthed at the same wharf from which the Magdalen Island steamship operated, with the hope that the cordwood might be sold for use on the Islands where no wood supply was available. The business of selling green cordwood to fish smoke-houses on the Halifax waterfront was grim.

However, there was a good supply of birch and maple cordwood along the Eastern Shore, and if old Abe just happened to fall for the smoke-house line, he could well be delayed a week trying to dispose of it, while Mose would have a "free-for-all," peddling goods along the coast. It was a long, restless night for Captain Mose, knowing such a rival as Abe had got a start on him.

When the janitor released the big latch to open the Customs, Shipping and Excise Offices for business on Thursday morning, Mose was first to the wicket. The same bearded officer that had taken care of Abe's business just twenty-four hours before greeted Captain Mose and, looking on toward the doorway, saw the two other trading skippers fall in the line up. These he also recognized as Captain Mason of the *Nannie O'Hara* and Captain Hodson of the *Maud G.*

"I see here, Captain Griffin, you've cleared from the port of

Isaac's Harbor. Did you sign on a crew at that port, sir?"

"No shipping master's office open for this season," was the reply. "Our crew list, sir, is John Musson, mate; Asa Gook, seaman; Dugan Tanning, seaman; Slim Lamey, cook; all from Gold Valley."

"Thanks, Captain, I'll just list them on our copy of the inward report."

"The vessel was built at Shelburne, N.S., and is now registered in Guysborough, N.S., forty tons net."

"You'll be taking out a Clearance Permit in a day or so, Captain, so the fees will be held now waiting harbor and wharfage bills," and *clump* went the big iron stamp on the copies of the inward report and receipt.

The captain received his copies and was told he was free to discharge and load cargo for any Canadian port on the East Coast. Mose lost no time looking for a sale for the cordwood so as to get rid of it, and to make the ship ready to take on cargo for more profitable business. The actual cause of his having the cordwood was to assist people that had only this means of earning a few dollars during the long winter. They probably never saw the money, but it served to pay for necessities that the trading skipper would purchase and transport for them, having of course, to get his own charges out of the deal, which constituted the ups and downs of coastal trading. As Captain Mose figured, the Magdalene & Gulf Shipping Company's agent bought the cargo on the basis that it would be crosspiled in the company's yard. This meant plenty of work for the entire crew plus a couple of beachcombers that hung around the wharves, in order to have the vessel ready to take on freight first crack o'dawn on Monday morning.

With a fresh breeze from the southwest, the *Western Belle* set sail and left Jeddore at two o'clock Thursday afternoon, and sailed down shore for about twelve miles, anchoring at a sheltered inlet named Southwest Cove, in the Ship Harbor area, to discharge twenty hogshead of fishery salt, some lobster rope and flour. Things were running, well, just too easy for Abe! Something was making him fidgety and uncomfortable. It was nothing but just being lonesome for the presence of that rival friend, Captain Mose. All day Friday, small sailboats and rowboats came in off the islands and neighboring inlets to replenish supplies — a puncheon of molasses had to be hoisted on deck and tapped, and if anybody complains about the service of getting the week's grocery supply checked through the cashier of a modern foodliner today, then think of the service Reuben Zinck was offering, drawing cold molasses through a half-inch wood spigot on the open deck of a trading schooner, on the south east coast of Nova Scotia during the month of March. The sun had gone over the hills and, as far as Southwest Cove was concerned, had set for the day.

The western slope shaded the inlet early in the day. It was actually dark when the last of the people had left. The cargo hatches were put on and covered while the crewmen swept and cleaned up the deck.

Abe amused himself by lashing the molasses puncheon securely, and before going below for supper, made a special survey of wind and weather conditions. A fresh southwest breeze was carrying some scattered moist clouds across the sky. It was semi-moonlight — about the last of a full moon which was partly shut off from what appeared to Abe as the making up of an accumulation of moisture and wind which would eventually bring on that blanket of fog so common to this coast. With the vessel at anchor in such a sheltered spot, it was not necessary to keep a watch on deck, so all hands ate supper together, discussed the pros and cons of the day and were enjoying a good smoke. By this time the wind had increased sufficiently to cause the fore and main halyards to start up a *tap, tap,* against the spars. When the sails are lowered and furled the throat halyards are stretched quite close to the masts, and further tightened by the moisture in the air. A rising wind will set them moving with a pulsating *tap, tap, tap,* that can go on for hours. With these indications Captain Abe worked out a weather forecast that supported his decision to get the schooner underway without further delay, and to proceed a distance approximately twelve miles to Ship Harbor — a much more convenient place to be, both from the point of business and shelter. Consequently he gave that old familiar command:

"Aye, below there — underway."

It brings all hands out, sails are hoisted, anchor weighed and secured on the bow. By ten o'clock that evening, the *Western Belle* was heaving and swaying in the broad Atlantic. She passed close under Cape Owl and the flash of the revolving light illuminated the sails and deck, and made the bow-wave glisten like a snowdrift. Mate Publicover steered the schooner with the steering wheel out on the open deck, and quite often, while making the passage out past the Friar Isle, got his face sprayed with clear, cool, salt water blowing back over the decks from the foaming bow wave.

Abe was in another world. Down in the cabin a series of sheets of paper tacked on a piece of wide board was the record of the day's transactions that had to be brought up to date in the books, which only a trading schooner captain could do and understand. It was important business, but soon lost its priority when Mate Publicover bellowed the request down the companionway asking for help on deck with the main sheet, announcing that the mainsail had to be jibed over, so as to maintain the required compass course to round Nicholl Island and proceed in to East Ship Harbor Government Wharf.

Abe quickly put the set of books, as they were, on his bunk — the one place on board ship at sea where you can best depend on putting any ordinary parcel of almost anything, and find it all in one piece when you do get back to catching up with it. Captain Abe's bearded face projected out of the companionway with the right timing to stop a shower of salt, cold spray. He used his cap to wipe the water off his forehead and eyes, made a sweep of the horizon from each side and ahead, to assure himself the vessel's position was correct, and went to the large wood bit-head to stand by the main sheet. The captain's local knowledge of the surroundings and approaches to Ship Harbor, aided by the semi-moonlight conditions, satisfied him it was now time to alter course to enter the Harbor.

"Bring her over, Bill," ordered the captain.

As Bill turned the wheel over to port, the old *Western Belle* veered to port and began to bring the wind aft across the stern sections. Finally, she disposed of the port list and in a relaxed motion, straightened herself to an even keel. This was of short duration — her veering to port at this point had brought the wind to blow on board over the port side, instead of the starboard side as it had done all the way from Southwest Cove and then, all of a sudden, over she listed to starboard and the sails and ropes groaned under the renewed stress applied as the sails again filled with wind.

"Steady on northwest by north, Bill," came up the captain as he eased off main and fore-sheets to a better trim for the run up harbor.

After the schooner had passed Nicholl Island and entered more sheltered water, the heave and roll were lost to a steady motion

15

which, particularly at night, makes it difficult to be sure you are really moving through the water. Approaching a wharf under sail at night requires tact and judgment. This, however, was not causing Abe too much concern; he had done it so many times that it became more or less a matter of routine. With just about one mile to go Captain Abe ordered the jib and mainsail lowered and furled. By the time this was done, the outline of the red shed on the head of the wharf was in view, about one quarter of a mile away. Fleet-footed Jack was picked to be ready to jump ashore on the wharf when the vessel came sufficiently close. He would then take a mooring line and secure the end to the wharf posts so that the vessel could be stopped and eased alongside.

"Lower away the jumbo and foresail," roared Abe.

These two sails fell in on deck and were left in that manner while the crew all stood by for mooring up at the wharf. She carried head-way very well, and was moving ahead quite slowly when she arrived at the wharf. Jack, who had himself perched on the sheer pole, above the rail and just below the first ratline, was all ready, and when the wharf looked about ten feet away and at a lower level than where he was perched, he made the take-off and landed safely on all fours on the wharf, picked himself up and got the bight, or eye, of the mooring-rope over the jetty post. From there on, it was a simple matter to even up bow and stern lines — a couple of springs and the *Western Belle* snuggled up to a safe berth. After the foresail and jumbo were furled, Captain Abe stood in the companionway with another half-gallon jug and shouted:

"Mugs, aft."

Seaman Zinck arrived back on the run, with four white mugs. Into each gurgled a good rugged snort of black rum.

"There's a night-cap now," and Abe's last command for the day was: "Tell the cook, breakfast at seven, sharp."

At six-thirty a.m. Saturday, the cook came on deck to blow the whistle for breakfast. He was greeted, as far as the weather was concerned, with a strong southerly wind and rain. That meant no cargo hatches would be opened under these conditions — driving rain would get down below and damage dry packages and grain cargo. Captain Abe was expecting that sort of weather and met the situation consoled with the attitude of "make the best of it, and like it".

The main topic over the breakfast table was the use of hardwood for fish smoking. Abe brought the subject up, knowing quite well

16

that when he got a little farther down the coast in the wooded areas, he would be faced with the business of finding a market for at least one cargo of the product. Caleb Madera had spent some time working at fish processing plants, and recalled the fish being dipped in a vegetable-dye coloring solution, with the smoke applied to the fish made from choice chips and sawdust. Abe's tactics were to listen to all sides and say little himself until he returned to Halifax to get definite information. There was one thing about a cordwood cargo of which he was positive, and that was that it could be handled during rainy weather without a worry. He knew Captain Mose was discharging cargo in Halifax while he was idling the day away.

About 10:00 a.m. two men came down and inquired for the captain. They were escorted to the cabin, Abe's *sanctum sanctorum.*

"Good morning, men!" greeted the skipper, "Kind of wet going for the week-end, I reckon."

"Yes, Captain, good to wash away the odd snowdrift and cut the ice up. Which way you headin' now, Captain?"

"Eastbound for a few days yet, then turning back to Halifax. What's on your minds?"

"We operate the box and barrel mill up river and got a surplus of stock piled up. We'd like to get a consignment up to that biscuit and candy manufacturer in Halifax as soon as possible."

"That's our line, my friends," came back the captain, "only too glad to make a dicker with you. Sounds like you been working steady all winter to be piled up like that."

It didn't take long to settle the freight charge with the agreement to start loading eight a.m. Monday. Abe and the boys had a snort or two, and all were happy over the charter. After dinner the entire crew got in the cargo hold, re-piled bags of flour, bundles of hay and what have you, so as to make all available space to load barrel staves and box shooks. This was what Abe needed to avoid — carrying a load of hardwood back to Halifax.

ERMYNTHRUDE

L.B.JENSON
from a sketch by
Captain Claude Darrach

Built in Shelburne in 1902, *Ermynthrude* was a bank fishing schooner for fourteen years, and like *Western Belle*, ended her days as a coastal trader.

In the Hands of a
Tugboat Skipper

Chapter 2

Two p.m. Saturday saw the last sling of the hardwood checked ashore from the *Lucy B*. The harbor tugboat, *Togo*, was standing by and lost no time in securing alongside and moving the schooner from the Gulf Shippers' Wharf to a large ocean freight terminal pier. Directly under a derrick crane, steam puffed and whistles blew, as the crane swung out and began to lower large wooden crates of machinery down on the deck of the *Lucy B*. When Captain Mose took the charter with the Gold Valley Mining Corporation to deliver this equipment on the Government Pier at Gold Valley, he overlooked the one thing that was facing him square between the two eyes at that very moment — the weight of the crates and the limited capacity of the *Lucy B.'s* cargo-lifting equipment. However, there was no getting out from under now — there it was, according to schedule and without effort, lowered down and placed, some on deck and some in the hold of the *Lucy B*. Before Captain Mose had a chance to wipe the sweat from his forehead, *toot, toot* went the tugboat whistle.

"You are all ready to move out now, Captain. The barquentine *William Farrow* moves in this berth in a few minutes. Cast off right away."

Mose was not the man to get excited quickly but he was having trouble now to keep in step with this big ship and tugboat routine. Three sharp *toots* on the tugboat whistle and away went the *Lucy*, stern first, out from the berth. Minutes after she cleared the entrance to the dock, along came two tugboats with the large *William Farrow*, heading in under the same derrick crane and toward the berth the *Lucy* had just made vacant. Once out on the harbor, into open water, Mose breathed a sigh of relief and his heart-beat resumed its normal speed.

"To Boake and Bennet Wharf, Captain," was Mose's order to the tugboat master.

The old tugboat master was doing his own wheeling, and was just in the act of twisting off a big chew of Mike McQuidd chewing

19

tobacco — a special brand of tobacco blended in Ireland, which some ship master had presented him with, in appreciation of a good job of berthing. So, with a jaw full of fresh tobacco and a wheel to manoeuver, the skipper was prompt in acknowledging Mose's order, but in regular tugboat fashion, which was a short blast of the whistle. This could be done in a split second, by jerking a taut rope lanyard dangling over the steering wheel. Mose was looking up from the deck of the *Lucy* to the open bridge of the tug, awaiting a verbal answer, when the shrill *toot* of the whistle gave his nerves a jolt that he was not braced for. To top things off, down over his face and shoulders came the spray of hot liquid steam that had been blown out with the *toot*. Mose saw that the schooner was headed for Boake and Bennet's Wharf and said no more. He turned to observe his own crew and see that they were ready for coming alongside, and noticed that young Slim Lamoy was head and neck in a crate of machinery when he, the cook, should have been below preparing supper. It did not take long for Mose to persuade Lamoy to get below and on the job.

"You want to berth bow out, Captin?" called up the tugboat master.

"That'll be fine, Cap, if you'll oblige," Mose replied, and with that the tugboat wheel spun over to starboard, the schooner's bow started swinging, engine-room bells jingled, and the big, heavy-duty propellor of the *Togo* churned up water. Ropes strained and groaned, and finally the *Lucy* came to a stop, snug up against the south side of Boake and Bennet's Wharf. The tug's lines were released.

"You'll get the bill Monday morn, Captain, thanks for the job."

Toot, toot, toot and away went the *Togo* for another move.

"Not me for the life of a tugboat skipper," pondered Mose. "Them fellers sure know tugboats and big ships and are not afraid to move them about."

While the crew evened up the mooring lines and put fenders between the pilings and the schooner's side, Captain Mose made a close survey of the crates. Twelve-and-one-quarter hundred-weight, sixteen hundredweight and so on, read the markings on the crates. Mose looked over the masts and rigging of the *Lucy*, and large drops of sweat ran down his cheeks as he thought of the arrival at Gold Valley and the problem of landing the machinery. Except for the hand-lever type mechanical windlass for heaving up the anchors, the only other lifting device on board these coastal

20

schooners was the crude arrangement of a horizontal drum supported by a wooden frame-work, fastened about four feet off the deck, just forward of the mainmast amidships. The drum was about eighteen inches in diameter. A strong iron band, furnished with elongated dog-teeth, was fitted on each end of the drum. This rode over the teeth as the drum was hand-cranked in a revolving motion to wind up the rope-lead from the purchase blocks, the hinged bar falling in the recess of each tooth to prevent the drum from taking a reverse motion and dropping the lift. This worked well to a capacity of up to one thousand pounds, but beyond that Mose knew he had to come up with something special.

Lamoy poked his head out of the forecastle now and blew a shrill note from a small metal whistle, the signal to come and get it. Before anyone had been served at the table, young Lamoy announced his findings in the large crate — fine, rugged-looking crusher gear. "Guysboro County might turn to a Klondike when that gear gets working. Think I'll stake off a claim when we return home." Mose came to the conclusion that Lamoy was more of a miner type than a sailor, and reckoned that if ever the machinery got ashore, Lamoy would be following it to the pit head.

It had been a busy and interesting day for the crew, although the weather, as also in Ship Harbor, was rainy with a breeze from the south. However, tomorrow was Sunday. Captain Mose was to have dinner ashore with relatives. Tonight there was Acker's Dime Theatre, a good stage show and a silent Western. The bars were open until midnight Saturday, so the order of the day was "wash and shave for a night in the big City". Captain Mose agreed to "stay and keep ship for tonight, but Sunday night someone else must plan to keep watch".

Young Slim Lamoy had looked forward to this for a long time. He was not the type to waste time lying on board an old schooner in a port like Halifax, so when the gang climbed over the sheer pole and onto the wharf, Slim was there, wide awake and raring to go. He got a big kick out of the Western, and believed the Indians with the bows and arrows had the advantage over the white man with the gun. No smoke or noise, no give-away — clearly the thing for shooting sea-birds along the shore at home. When the boys went to the bar for a nightcap, Slim chose the confectionery store and filled up with ice cream and a week-end supply of fancy candy. When they arrived on board, they met with a pleasant surprise — Captain Mose had made a wild duck stew, with dumplings. With the idea in mind of sleeping in until nine a.m. everybody, including the night watchman on the wharf, had his fill of duck stew, and called it the end of a week well spent.

Sunday at East Ship Harbor was a quiet day for the crew of the *Western Belle*. They went to church in the evening, joined in a social sing-song and a "pass-round" of tea and cake, and were back on board by eleven p.m.

Monday morning brought a strong NW wind with a temperature just above freezing. In Halifax the *Lucy B.* received teamload after teamload of barreled and bagged flour, oats, bran and a variety of packaged goods, about forty hogshead of salt, rope, building and furnishing material, several barrels of apples, sugar, tea, and kerosene oil, but Mose deliberately drew the line at molasses until the weather got warmer.

If Captain Mose Griffin had a nerve-racking afternoon on Saturday, Captain Abraham Young was sharing the same fate at Eastern Sheet Harbor on Monday. Boats were alongside, and people were coming down the wharf to purchase anything from lobster fishing rope to two gallons of molasses. Zinck had abandoned the use of the measure, and was allowing the molasses to run directly from the spigot to the jug — quite a time-saving arrangement. At ten o'clock, the jingle of soft-toned bells caused Abe to look up the wharf to see a large hay wagon, drawn by a pair of oxen, and loaded sky-high with barrel staves and box shooks.

Two local men were hired to help keep up with the discharging and loading operations. Captain Abe had the familiar old tally board under his arm all day, and was to and from the cabin, where he kept a shaggy sail duck-bag in which the cash receipts of the day were held. Sometimes a good customer rated a swig from the little brown jug. Several traded a half-barrel of foxberries for supplies. This was where the tally board came in, to record the detailed transaction when a trade was made. No one was available to check the amount of shooks and staves that were being loaded, and Captain Abe ordered them piled evenly and neatly across the hold and up against the bulkhead, laying a tier of shooks and alternating

22

with a tier of staves. In this way, he could make a rough check himself at the end of the day and be satisfied the amount was reasonably correct as to what the load actually totalled for freight charges. In all, three hay-wagon loads of shooks were taken on board, and about eight tons of supplies disposed of. Abe agreed with the suggestion of the mill "super", to call in on the return voyage and load all the shooks and staves the schooner could carry, sealed the deal with a couple of snorts, lighted the cabin lamp and called it a very good day.

Salt cod, potatoes and parsnips, all garnished with sizzling hot pork-fat was the supper menu; boiled rice, with raisins floating deep in fresh cream, was the dessert. Two men that were hired to help with the cargo remained for supper and complimented Millwood Jack on his cooking.

The *Lucy B.* had a good day in Halifax. She had all the under-deck cargo stowed and was to move to the oil company to load twenty wooden 40 gallon barrels of kerosene oil. These would be carried on deck and would just about complete her load, allowing her to get away from Halifax early next day. Captain Griffin was through supper early and was off to satisfy his curiosity as to what the *Maud G.* and *Nannie O'Hara* were doing. The *O'Hara* had undergone extensive repairs during the winter and was fitted with a special opening in the starboard bow section just above the waterline — an arrangement for loading long logs or long-sawn timber. Being fitted in this manner, it was quite easy for Captain Morris to get the charter to carry the long, creosoted timber from Halifax to Sheet Harbor for use in building the new Government Wharf. This charter would consist of several trips, as Captain Mose learned when he met Captain Hodson from the *Maud G.* The *Maud G.* was loaded with salt and empty mackerel barrels. The Captain had just left the Customs Office with clearance papers and was sailing within the hour for Port Bickerton where the entire cargo was consigned. The distance from Halifax to Port Bickerton, approximately ninety miles, would take about twenty-four hours' sailing.

Captain Mose returned to the *Lucy B.*, well satisfied with the type of cargo he was carrying, called the three crew members back to his cabin and gave them an advance bonus of five dollars each, well knowing their funds were limited. This, he knew, would make it possible for them to do a little special shopping, particularly when they were about ready to sail for home. It was a pleasant surprise, and one hour later the three were on Barrington Street on a real shopping excursion. Young Lamoy lost no time in buying a rugged pair of high-laced leather boots, having in mind the idea of hard rock mining. However, it was quite evident when they returned to the schooner and were finding suitable storage for the parcels, that all had visited and done some shopping at a ladies' wear store. Early Tuesday morning when the *Lucy B.* was moving to the oil docks, the *Nannie O'Hara* set sail from the lumberyard pier and was on her way for Sheet Harbor.

After getting the schooner secured alongside the oil dock, Captain Griffin saw the oil barrels being lowered on deck, and started off for the Customs Office. The procedure of clearning the schooner for a local port was short and simple. Mose left the Customs House and went a few blocks down town to a large wholesale import-and-export liquor store, and half an hour later arrived back at the oil dock. He made the return trip from the export house in a flat canvas-covered, horse-drawn delivery wagon, passed a couple of wooden cases and a half dozen half-gallon brown jugs on board the schooner, paid the teamster his fee and checked with Mate John Musson regarding the readiness of the schooner to sail. Musson assured him all deck cargo would be secured and lashed before getting out in open water. At this, Mose ordered the vessel cast off, and on the way.

The light westerly breeze was made to order for a sailing vessel eastbound, so no time was lost in getting all sails set and underway. When the *Lucy* rounded Thrumcap buoy at the eastern approaches to Halifax Harbor, the sails of the *Nannie O'Hara* could be seen about ten miles ahead. Asa Gook came and took the wheel, and was given that old familiar course "East by south, Asa". "East by south," repeated Asa back to the captain. It's a fixed routine in large and small ships alike, whenever there is an exchange in wheelsmen, the course is repeated clear and loud, by the man being relieved and by the man taking over the wheeling job.

It was midday now, and a checkup revealed all four vessels were under sail. The veteran captain, Abe Young, sailed from East

Ship Harbor at eight a.m. and was standing in between Yankey Jack and Taylor's Goose Shoals, to pass Sheet Rock and Western Islands, to berth at a government pier inside Malagash Island. This was a community on the western shore of Sheet Harbor, which was an enterprising area, with a couple of general stores, and some successful fishermen. The wind was moderate and Abe was conning the *Western Belle* close past some dangerous shoals to save time and distance. Sheet Rock was rounded at one-thirty p.m. and a short run of two-and-one quarter miles brought the schooner off the Mushaboom pier. The port anchor was let go — a full length of sixty fathoms of chain directly off the seaward end of the pier. This aided in turning the vessel's bow seaward and allowing her to be backed, stern first, in alongside the long, narrow pier, a very convenient arrangement for getting a sailing vessel away from the wharf, particularly when the wind is blowing in on the pier. Captain Abe was never to be underestimated for his qualities of seamanship. From 3 p.m. until dark, business went as usual. The two general stores were the sole purchasers of food stuff, hay and animal feed. Salt and rope were peddled to the fishermen. Abe was approached for the first time to accept a consignment of hardwood, but had a definite reason to ask that it might be held off for this trip, because of the more profitable and fast moving cargo — the box wood and barrel staves.

Abe did have to make the supreme sacrifice that night, of resorting to a wash and shave, and with two of the crewmen, attended a concert and auction pie sale in aid of the village schoolhouse. Captain Abe filled a couple of empty pint flasks with the necessary vitamins to keep a sea-faring character's spirits in the mood to sit through a school children's program. However, as he expected, he soon made a rendezvous with a couple of old acquaintances, and after paying the doorman for tickets for his two crew members and the two old fishermen friends from Boutilier's Island, he suggested that the two should join him outside for a smoke. The program was well advanced when they finally did enter the old schoolhouse and found some chairs in the back row. By this time they were in a mood to cheer and clap any number that appeared on the stage. After the finale and the singing of "The King," the stage was transformed to an auctioneer's block where a handsomely decorated display of boxes and baskets containing home-made pies and cakes were to be auctioned off.

There was lots of keen competition and high bidding,

particularly when a fancy package came up that could well have been baked by one of the pretty young ladies, with probably, several admirers. The reward of making the purchase was to sit with the lady whose name would be announced by the auctioneer when the bid was closed. Tea and cocoa would be served and the cakes eaten. Captain Abe, on principle, had to get in on the bidding and be sure to get a knock down. On a couple of occasions he teased some of the young fellows by sticking in a high bid when he knew for sure that one certain chap would mortgage his next year's salary to get his beloved's special cake.

Finally, a very neat basket came up, the auctioneer put in a couple of high salesmanship plugs and announced,

"She starts at one dollar fifty."

Captain Abe upped it to two dollars, the parish clergyman made the next bid,

"Two fifty, Mr. Auctioneer."

The auctioneer, an old vet at the game, capitalized on the situation.

"Well, well, here we have two distinguished guests competing for this handsome basket. Will this decide the Queen of the Ball and bring the highest bid?"

"Three dollars!" pipes up one of the men from Boutilier's Island.

Abe took a side glance at his friend and wondered if it was just the few swigs from the flask or if this was a special package he also should go after. The parson raised his hand and upped his bid to four dollars, and before Abe could get in again, a young fellow came up with an even five dollars. The auctioneer announced the bid for the five and attempted some remarks when Abe roared,

"Make that even five, seven dollars."

This brought a round of applause that made the old building tremble. The auctioneer pointed to the remaining packages and called for a speed-up in bidders. The parson stood up, but before he spoke Abe upped his own bid to eight dollars right from where he sat.

"Eight she is, eight she was, going! going! gone! Gone to Captain Young, this masterpiece," and reaching in the basket, he picked out a small white card and announced that Captain Young and Miss Dugan, the school teacher, would sit at the end of the guest table and enjoy the contents of the package.

Abe was glad now he had gone to the trouble of shaving and donning some clean clothes before leaving the schooner. All he needed now was a good bracer of vitamins from the flask before joining the teacher at the head of the table. He had a hunch this would call for some remarks. Abe had no worry about keeping his speech in order when on board ship, but to face an audience of school children, their parents, the teenagers, teacher, and above all, the parson and his wife, was a situation where Captain Abe would have to navigate with caution. He and Boutilier managed to get in the clothes closet for long enough to take the required supply of vitamins, and they slipped the empty flask in the pocket of the parson's raccoon coat. Boutilier patted Abe on the shoulder and wished him luck with the teacher's cooking. Abe took the gesture with all sincerity, little knowing that he had been "framed" by his bosom friend, Boutilier, a trustee; the auctioneer, a school board member; and the parson, who conveniently teamed up to prompt Abe's bidding.

The last basket to go caused the hottest bidding between the young bachelors of the village and topped Abe's bid by two-fifty. This was from a young chap home on shore leave off a large ocean-going South Sea sealing schooner. He could have stopped off at several larger port cities and enjoyed a holiday in the bright lights, but had a much greater attraction at home, and did not hesitate to prove his point by making that attraction the Queen of the party. This took care of both ends of the table and the hoarse voice of the auctioneer was heard requesting all to be seated. The parson asked the blessing and followed by complimenting the two couples who had gained the honor of occupying the end seats.

The long table was a picture, being lined with all the prettily decorated baskets and boxes. Tea and cocoa were served, and all were digging in when the trustee, Mr. Boutilier, got up and thanked everyone for the support in making the party a success. He asked for a few words from the end seats, taking particular care to be facing the Queen's end of the table and, addressing the young man as "Walter", suggested he might tell them about his seagoing experiences. This brought a round of applause as Walter stood up.

"Mr. Chairman and everybody, the whole truth about seagoing . . ." he hesitated, put his arm over his Queen's shoulder, drew her head against his side, and went on to say, "it's best when you get home and have the pleasure of eating a delicious cake with the Queen of the Party."

When Captain Young was called on to speak, he got a thundering roar of applause. He addressed the chairman, his reverence and everybody, looked down at the pretty school teacher and back at the people.

"I can't tell whether it's that pretty dress, or the trimmin's on the basket, but something's got the wind knocked out of me sails. This is a lovely party and I never tasted a nicer cake in me life. And the thing I want to do is congratulate the children on the singing. There must be a good church choir in this village."

With a sly glance toward the parson, Abe assured them that a good church choir was a fine thing, since it keeps the congregation awake. He chanced another look at the parson and seated himself beside the teacher again. Mr. Boutilier arose and thanked both men for the speeches, announced the hour was getting late and asked for volunteers for putting the schoolroom ship-shape for classes in the morning. The parson arranged his departure to close in on Captain Young at the doorway and whispering a word of thanks for the souvenir, suggested maybe he had it coming to him. And so ended the school concert.

"One of Three Things got to Happen"   Chapter 3

Once Captain Abe arrived out in the cool, clear atmosphere and fresh westerly breeze, his mind wandered back to the sea, and visions of the *Lucy B.* scudding down the coast came like a ghost in the night. And, sure enough, it was midnight. Twelve hours previously the *Lucy* had rounded Thrumcap and was well down the coast. She had averaged five knots and was off the White Islands, heading for the Liscomb fairway buoy to shape a course in past the Black Prince Shoals and on into Little Liscomb to discharge the first of her cargo. Only the dark of the night prevented Abe from seeing the *Nannie O'Hara* from the roadway, as he walked down to the pier. The *Nannie* was inside Western Islands and heading for Watt Point as her destination at Sheet Harbour, passing at the moment less than two miles from the *Western Belle*. The *Maud G.* arrived at Port Bickerton at nine p.m. and would be discharging her cargo in the morning.

The *Western Belle* had two more calls to make on the east-bound run: Necum Teuch and Fisherman's Harbor. Captain Young arrived on board to find all hands awake. Visitors were on board and just leaving. Abe suggested a night-cap for the boys, so they all arrived aft at his cabin. The mate, sensing a method in the old man's move, soon got the idea when he watched Abe change from shore-going togs to the home-spun trousers and heavy sweater.

"Can't fly on one wing, boys, fill 'em up again."

They did — the four visitors and three crew members. He gave the mate a wink and announced that he believed, while the extra help was at hand, they could hoist the sails and be on the way. A half-hour later, the two big sails, mainsail and foresail, were hoisted, and *clinkty, clank* went the pump lever windlass heaving up the anchor. The anchor lay a good three hundred feet directly off the wharf, so the four men went ashore, released the schooner's mooring lines and as the chain cable was hove in, the vessel slowly moved off from the wharf. When the anchor-chain hung perpendicular from the hawse pipe, the jumbo was hoisted.

29

Captain Young went to the wheel, spun it over to port and trimmed the fore-sheet. He felt the old schooner make a head motion, then trimmed in the main sheet and towed the anchor free from its grip on the bottom. A rapid burst of *clinkty, clank,* for a few minutes, then the mate shouted,

"Anchor's aweigh."

"Good," replied the captain, "hoist the outer jib, light the port and starboard side lights."

Twenty-five minutes later, and two and one-half miles, the *Western Belle* was passing under the flash of Sheet Rock Light. The captain calculated the speed at six knots and was quite content to spend a couple of hours at the wheel while the crew got some sleep. The *Western Belle* could be expected to arrive at Necum Teuch, twenty-five miles away, not later than eight in the morning.

Captain Abe put in his two hours' wheeling and at three p.m. was relieved by Mate Publicover. The schooner was heading on an east magnetic course. The captain instructed the mate to continue on the east course until reaching Bassoon Reef bell buoy; then alter to NNE and call him out again when Halibut Island came abeam. If the breeze held up, that would be about five a.m., and daylight.

The wind became quite moderate after daylight and the schooner *Lucy B.* came to anchor in the passage between Redman Head and Liscomb Island. Several small boats came alongside and Captain Mose settled down to business. Sugar, flour, salt and several items of the cargo were disposed of. There was no let-up until four p.m.

Captain Abe's *Western Belle* managed to hold enough wind and sailed to anchorage at Ship Rock Island. Only the small head sails were lowered. Merchants from Ecum Secum, Smith's Cove, Harrigan Cove and other neighboring villages came and just about cleaned out the *Western Belle* cargo. Some salt and a consignment of packages had to be taken to Fisherman's Harbor and that would be the turning point, then she would stop on the return voyage and pick up the balance of box wood and barrel-staves for Halifax.

Several miles separated the rival skippers. Both were faced with the same state of affairs: that of being at anchor, ready and anxious to get going, but with no wind for sailing. However, both recognized what would follow the still, calm weather and were alert to get moving at the first sign of wind. It came about 8 p.m. Moderate south-east wind filled the sails, and ropes commenced *pit-pat* movements. No time was lost getting anchors aweigh and attending to the operation of tacking the schooners out past the dangerous shoals during the dark hours. By midnight the cumbersome *Western Belle* had tacked off-shore to a position eight miles south-east of Beaver Island Light. With the wind veering from south-east to south, she could come about and make good an easterly course, and head for the entry to Fisherman's Harbor.

The trim *Lucy B.* soon tacked out through the narrow passage between Liscomb Island and the Tobacco Ledges. Midnight found the *Lucy* rounding Isaac's Harbor whistle buoy, heading N1/2W for Holly Point Light, and home. At two a.m. sails were lowered, furled and the schooner was all secure on the north side of the Gold Valley Government Wharf. The Captain and young Lamoy both departed from the ship and went home. The others, more interested in much needed sleep, turned in. Every old dog along the narrow roadway, from the wharf to the Lamoy homestead, knew and barked a greeting of welcome home to young Slim. Each one of them got a piece of fancy candy and a "shut-up the barking" command.

The entire household was awakened to see the new high laced boots and to hear the first-hand news of the mining machinery they had on board.

It was broad daylight when the old *Western Belle* reached anchorage at Fisherman's Harbor. This is less than four miles from Holly Point, and the tall masts of the *Lucy B.* were a welcome sight to Captain Abe as he sailed the *Western Belle* across the entrance of Gold Valley for Fisherman's Harbor. It was now nine a.m. and a strong, southerly breeze blowing. By three p.m. the *Western Belle* had discharged all cargo consigned there and Abe had a few drinks with the boys, just to wish them luck with the season's fishing. He was given a special treat, renowned at that particular port: a gallon jug of preserved "bakeapples". These berries grow in a cluster similar to blackberries, are gold in color, found on exposed moist barrens, and have a unique and wonderful flavor.

Four p.m. saw the *Western Belle* get underway and head for Gold Valley. Reason one, a storm was now in the making and Gold Valley was a sheltered harbor; reason two, Captain Abe Young was anxious to meet his beloved rival, Captain Mose Griffin. When the *Western Belle* shot in along the south side of the Government Wharf, Abe sensed an atmosphere of anxiety, so he lay low on any of the hasty, sarcastic remarks he generally came up with in greeting his rival friend. Thirty-five feet, the width of the wharf, was all that separated the two schooners. When Captain Abe stepped ashore, Captain Mose was there to shake hands and welcome him in a sheltered berth until the storm blew over. Mate Publicover had the main cargo hatch open on board *Western Belle* just long enough for Captain Mose to see the box-wood and barrel-stave cargo.

"What's that I see there, Captain?" queried Mose.

"Smoked fish boxes," came back Abe without blinking an eyelash.

"Big business that fish smoking. Big demand for hardwood, so I hear; and that being the case, surely they'll be needing packing boxes. And what's all this cargo you have, Captain Griffin? Fancy lettering on them crates, ain't it?"

Walking across the wharf, toward the *Lucy,* old weather-beaten Abe focused his eyes on what he described as a snarl. A strained and twisted cargo winch, broken purchase blocks, and a large crate with a heavy strap showing signs of a weight that had proved too much for the capacity of the *Lucy's* lifting gear. It was not easy for Mose, but he admitted to Abe he was in trouble.

"That I see," replied Abe. "Yes, Mose, in trouble you are."

In making the last remark, Mose recognized a drift of sarcasm in the tone of Abe's voice. That he accepted, knowing quite well Abe would have his fun but would never sail from the wharf until the snarl was cleared up.

The day was getting along toward the time for the evening meal. Abe saw and summed up the state of affairs Mose had brought on himself, and came up with:

"Boy, what you need right now is 'Reconnin' Vitamins', I believe I got some over in me cabin, come along."

Mose took the hint.

"Captain Young, since this is my home port, let the honors be on me. You come on board my vessel."

"Have it your way, Captain. On such occasions I ain't in the habit of saying no."

They climbed on board the *Lucy B.* and down to the cabin. Mose lighted the oil lamp that swung in a brass gimbal. By this time Abe had seated himself in the captain's easy chair, making a couple of surges, port and starboard, to test its stability.

"Not a bad chair, Mose. Choppy weather when you'd have to lash him down, I reckon."

Mose by this time was head and shoulders under the mattress of his large double bunk. But not for long, and when he emerged and stood up, he was holding a fancy decorated long-neck, twenty-six ounce bottle. Tinfoil and ribbon glistened on the neck, a sprig of purple heather was attached to the label which read, "Forty Years Old When Bottled". Mose's large hand twisted the fancy trimmings off, and reached to a shelf in his bunk where he brought out a cork screw. The long cork stopper was drawn, and as it broke the seal, *plunk!* went the rush of air that was drawn into the vacant space the cork had left. Glass tumblers were within reach in a neat rack along the bulkhead, and as Mose passed the bottle over to his guest, Abe with one hand picked out two tumblers, dropped one in Mose's lap and held the other up to the beam of light and poured himself a man-size slug. Mose did likewise, and *clink,* the tumblers came together in a gesture of "Good Sailing" as the two skippers proceeded to imbibe the famous Scotch brew. This cleared their throats for conversation and Mose made the start.

"Got meself in a terrible fix here, Abe. Hates to say it, but I'm stuck."

This was when Abe realized he held a trump card and began to figure how and what way he could play it best.

"I don't understand," said Abe, "how a man with such a fine choice for liquor could get in such a fix. That's beautiful stuff in that there bottle."

And as he was taking the bottle away from Mose for the second time, he looked Mose straight in the eye, and as if he didn't know, asked:

"Just what is the trouble, old boy? Ye think it's something you and me can't put right?"

"Look here, Abe, if you kin help me out of this mess I'll dance at yer weddin'."

"Well now, Mose, there ain't going to be any wedding for me, but I always enjoy watching a good dancer."

"A man with a mind like you, Abe, should live forever. Tell me the secret sometime — but let me describe me trouble, and come up with one of yer answers to cure the mess. Abe! I got a fine charter, big pay to fetch this here mining machinery down here, and now the lifting gear won't hoist the main piece of equipment ashore. Can't even lift it off the deck."

"That's a bad fix, old boy, how'd you come to get into that trouble? What weight is the gadget, anyhow?"

"A bit over a ton, Abe, and this afternoon we got a gang of men on the winch, and it tore off the deck and now it's out of commission."

"How does the price of that whiskey compare with the rum, Mose, and what brand is it?" Abe queried.

"Three H's, Highland Heather Honey. Now drink her down, Captain, and forget the cost. Let's hear what ye recommend to get this lot of machinery on the wharf."

Abe's big fist came down on the more slender shoulder of skipper Mose with a thud of assurance that the matter was simple, and with the first high tide tomorrow that load of wheels and gear would be on the wharf. Mose had confidence in Abe in spite of the affect the "Three H's" might be having, and at that he poured a couple of fingers in each of the empty tumblers and raised his for Abe to touch glasses and make it a deal. As the glasses came together, Mose said, "It's a deal and we'll split the profits." "No such thing, Mose, it's a deal and all the profits is yours. But I might ask a small favor from yourself some day." They shook hands, and agreed to be on the job at dawn.

Captain Abe arrived back on board his own vessel just in time to get in on a sizzling-hot moose steak. Evidently some wood choppers had found a large moose that had got its leg down a hole in the ice while crossing a lake and they had to kill the animal to get it out. The magistrate agreed it was the most humane thing to do. Friends the mate had visited ashore gave him a few steaks. Abe devoured his steak and a hot mug of tea, then went to his cabin, only to awake next morning to discover that he had slept all night in his heavy

34

shirt and homespun trousers. The boots and heavy sweater lay on a coil of rope in the corner.

Abe knew the lifting capacity of his own equipment, and was sure extra people would be on hand to help. But now, with the winch of the *Lucy* out of commission, something would have to be contrived as a substitute for it. The range of the rise and fall of tide, he knew, was six feet; he also knew that at high-tide the *Lucy B.'s* deck was level with the wharf. After an early breakfast of hot buns, coffee and baked beans specially browned and flavored with pork and molasses, Abe proceeded to the wharf ready to commence operations. Captain Griffin was just arriving from his home. They met, discussed the weather and reasoned out a forecast for the next twenty-four hours. Both found themselves looking down on the *Lucy's* deck where the heavy crate stood just aft of the main mast on the starboard side (the side to the wharf) and only a few feet away from the twisted and broken winch.

"Now Mose, here's what I'd do in this case. First, let go all that starboard main-mast rigging clear away from the dead eyes. To the cribbing of the wharf, fix a good strong wire strop. The main sheet is a strong triple purchase. Bring that and seize the boom block to the mainmast, well up the mast and the other end of the sheet, the drift end; secure it well to the wire strop down on the side of the wharf. Hook the main throat halyards to the crate, tie the drift end of the sheet and the down lead of the throat halyards together. Leave no slack whatever. Now you see, as the ship rises with the tide, the main sheet will spread out and when this happens the triple purchase will want more rope than the double throat purchase to lift the crate. Then with the foresail throat halyards hooked to the crate and leading down to the windlass, you can lift a bit there and take a lot of the stress off the main gear. With that rig, Mose, one of three things *got* to happen. You busts up the wharf, capsizes the schooner, or lifts up the crate."

Abe saw a sheepish look come over Mose's face, and changed the subject without further delay.

"Me throat's terrible dry and husky."

"Yes," agreed Mose, "and if ever I needed a drink in my life, it's now for sure."

They headed for the cabin of the *Lucy*. Mose said he felt ashamed of himself for being unable to think of that very same idea.

The two mates and several voluntary helpers were busy rigging and fixing Abe's rig. It went along quite well and while they were having the second wet of Three H's, the schooner gave a violent surge and they heard the groan of the ropes.

"There she sits tight on it now," remarked Abe. "And if you don't mind, there's a couple of swigs left in that fancy bottle. Let me have it, I'm taking a walk up the village, and I always likes to have a yarn with Deacon Slivers and leave him a little something to buy putty for the church windows — and a good hot toddy. It'll do him and Sarah good."

On the way up, he told Mate Publicover to bring the fore and main throat halyards of the *Western Belle* across the wharf, and as soon as the crate could be swung in over the wharf, to put the gang on and heave it over, off the *Lucy's* deck and onto the pier. Modest old Abe didn't want to be on the scene when the crate was brought ashore. After all, it was not his vessel that was discharging the cargo, and furthermore, the actual truth of his going ashore was to get on some high land where he could look out on the ocean and get a good check on the possibility of making the passage back to East Ship Harbor. The storm was blowing over and out of the area. He had had his fun with Captain Mose and was ready to proceed, pick up a nice cargo of box wood, and return to Halifax, where he and Captain Griffin would meet again. From what he did see of the ocean, the wind was coming from a westerly direction. The sea was moderately rough but improving, and so he decided that at two p.m. they would get underway, sail all night and maybe by noon next day could arrive at Ship Harbor, a distance of roughly seventy-five miles.

He dropped in on the Slivers' family, met and talked with some of the older residents, then stopped at Luke's little two-by-four grocery store to pick up a couple of pairs of hand-knit woolen socks. It was twelve o'clock, and a stone's throw from old Luke's store was the little brown schoolhouse. The doors had just opened to let classes out for dinner hour and, as usual, most of the kids dropped in at Luke's. In a matter of seconds, Captain Abe was surrounded by youngsters, large and small. He made some inquiries about the teachers, and accused one youngster of having a plug of tobacco in his pocket. That was a big attraction and brought the kids in a huddle. At this point he had Luke pass him a couple of cardboard boxes of penny candies, made sure each kid was treated, and gave the accused what was left in the box just to square matters; paid Luke for the sweets, and headed back for the schooner.

36

When he arrived at the wharf, two yokes of oxen were hitched to a large birch drag on which was lashed the crate that had caused Captain Mose so much grief. He made inquiries for Mose and found him on board the *Western Belle,* in the forecastle with his crew, paying a little tribute for the assistance they so willingly gave. Abe requested Mose to join him in the cabin as soon as he was free to leave the forecastle. Abe just had sufficient time to arrange his final act with Mose before sailing. When Mose reached the cabin of *Western Belle,* Abe had two fourteen-ounce white mugs and a half-gallon stone jug set up on a coil of rope that was as convenient as a coffee table at home today.

"I am sorry, Captain Griffin, I can't put on the dog with crystal tumblers and fancy bottles, but if you'll join me, I'd like to pour you a splash just for old times' sake."

"Happy to join you any time, Abe, but let me pour my splash."

"Tain't good manners for me not to pour your drink, on me own schooner."

By this time, a heavy splash landed smack in Mose's white mug and another of the same in the second mug. Before Abe got the jug back on an even keel he managed to slip an extra splash in the first mug before Mose could reach it. Captain Mose downed a couple of long swallows, and looked in the mug. He still had a couple of fingers left. He shook his head and pleaded with Captain Abe to accept some payment for getting him squared away with the crate.

"Mose, boy, I couldn't think of it — not at all."

But it was here old Abe played his trump card, and mildly came back at Mose to suggest that it would help him an awful lot if on the return voyage to Halifax the *Lucy B.* would stop at Dufferin Bay and Malagash Islands and pick up a deck load of cordwood — that smoke-house wood.

"Whatever profit you get is all yours, and when you call in the ports, you won't have any trouble getting the stuff if you mention I recommended you fer the business."

Having now been obliged to take the undesirable and bothersome stuff, Mose gained the required courage to finish what was left of the splash in the mug. He could feel himself beginning to "sort of float in the air." But when Abe announced that he was sailing within the hour, Mose developed a kind of lonesome feeling, and slipped up by letting Abe get another wee splash in his mug. The two heavy mugs came together with a flat *clank!* as each wished the other smooth sailing.

Abe went to the forecastle for dinner and Mose climbed on the wharf and proceeded on a bit of a zig-zag course homeward for his meal and an afternoon of relaxation to celebrate having got the mining machinery landed in accordance with the charter.

When Mose awoke that afternoon the sun was at a low altitude in the western sky and glancing seaward toward the horizon he could see the gleaming white sails of the *Western Belle*. A heavy ground swell, the aftermath of the storm, was still running high and occasionally the schooner lifted enough to show parts of her copper-painted bottom. Captain Mose was on land, and at home with beautiful surroundings, but to watch the old schooner surge along over the western horizon gave him that longing which only a fascination for the sea can produce. He wanted to be out there in company with his rival friend Captain Abe.

The day following the eventful unloading of the mining machinery at Gold Valley dawned with an atmosphere of new hope and adventure for the people of the entire community. The *Lucy B.* made the two-and-one-half mile trip via Harbor Island Passage and berthed at the Darby Point Government Wharf at nine o'clock to take on board barrels of salted mackerel. These were choice, large, fall fish, caught and cured during the months of November and December and deliberately held over for spring marketing as part of a budget plan. There being no fresh fish market available, all varieties of fish had to be salt-cured before sale. Looking at this from a dollar and cent point of view, it resulted in not more than four or five pay days per year. Therefore the sale of the fall catch at this time provided ready cash to pay for spring outfits to commence the spring fishing and also brought in the necessary money required for household necessities, until the end of the lobster season in the month of June, at which time the next cash settlement would take place.

Lobsters were delivered to canneries as they were caught and a lump sum payment made at the completion of the pack. The herring and in-shore cod fishing would follow and continue through the summer and autumn months.

At four o'clock the barreled mackerel were all securely stowed in the cargo hold, and with a very light southwest breeze, Captain Mose ordered all sails set in order to get back to Gold Valley to load empty wooden kerosene-oil barrels. These barrels would be stowed on deck full or empty. Oil barrels were a dangerous cargo and special ventilation was necessary if carrying oil below decks.

Although the sale of the mackerel was of financial importance to the fishermen, everything now was left to the master of the schooner who in this case was Captain Mose. On arrival at Halifax, he would approach the different merchants and make the decision to sell if a good price was offered. In the case of a low price, he might consign the lot to one or more commission merchants at Boston, Massachussetts, and get the returns by mail within one month after shipment.

It took almost three hours for the passage back to Gold Valley in the light breeze. On arrival there Mose soon discovered that the delivery of the mining machinery was having its effect on employment. He was not the least surprised when young Lamoy requested to be paid off. The Captain agreed to Lamoy's request and wished him a lucky strike that some day would make him a rich man. However, they were unable to hire a replacement at Gold Valley. The situation was relieved for the captain when two men wanted passage to Halifax. They were seamen going up to the Great Lakes for the summer shipping season, and one of them agreed to act as cook and work his passage to Halifax in that manner.

Saturday morning dawned with a light northeast wind, favorable for the *Lucy B.* to sail the nine-mile channel out to Isaac's Harbor fairway buoy, alter course westward over the forty mile voyage to Dufferin Bay, and on to the Malagash Islands to pick up the hardwood that Captain Abe so skillfully arranged. By noon the wind had become very moderate and had veered toward the south. The light southerly breeze carried the *Lucy* along slowly, and sundown saw her arrival at the pier in the sheltered Dufferin Bay. Loading cargo commenced at once and continued until ten o'clock when the last stick of the clumsy cordwood was taken off the wharf. Captain Mose set sail immediately for the short trip around Cape Beaver, on in past the famous Sheet Rock and to Malagash Islands, where he would be in readiness for a crack o'dawn start Monday morning.

The entry in the *Western Belle's* log book, dated noon Friday, recorded her arrival at East Sheet Harbor and went on to read that extra help was hired and loading operations commenced immediately. By six o'clock, the cargo hold was filled to the hatches with barrel staves and box shooks. The hired help were fed and paid for the work of assisting the loading, and by eight o'clock the *Western Belle* was underway and sailing outward through the harbor channel to round the fairway buoy and head westward on the forty-five mile trip to Halifax.

Once out in the open sea again and with a fresh southwest breeze and moderate ground-swell, the ropes and shrouds of the old schooner stretched and groaned under the strain, clear green sea-water spouted in through the lee scuppers and halfway across the deck, as she lurched and careened from the pressure of wind in the sails. Her bluff bows, cutting through the water at a good eight knots, spread the green water into two foaming breakers that continually rolled away, allowing the two black quarter-sections of the hull to wallow along with that smooth, free and easy movement typical of a schooner under sail.

A sail was sighted less than one mile ahead. It also was heading westward with all sheets trimmed close, as were those of the *Western Belle*. This was necessary in order to maintain a west by north track toward the entrance of Halifax Harbor. Occasionally it was also necessary to tack ship and stand off shore for a couple of miles to hold the track line. It was on one of these occasions that the two schooners came very close to each other, during crossing tacks, and Captain Abe was able to identify his companion as being Captain Hodson in the *Maud G.*, returning to Halifax from Port Bickerton.

Monday and Tuesday saw all four schooners berthed along the Halifax Waterfront. The *Lucy B.* went direct to the Gulf Island Trading Wharf to endeavour to get rid of the cordwood, and the *Maud G.* to the Oarlee Canning Company to load cases of empty cans, a variety of canning equipment and wood lobster crates — a very nice cargo of cannery supplies, required to get three of the coastal lobster canneries in operation when the season opened early in April. The ports of call for the deliveries were Queensport, Marie Joseph and Little Harbor. The *Nannie O'Hara* was at the lumberyard, loading material as per her charter for the Sheet Harbor Wharf, and the *Western Benne* went on to Bedford Basin to the chocolate and biscuit factory to discharge the box and barrel material.

The Boake and Bennet firm had sold many tons of fishery salt to two large fish-processing plants, on the condition that delivery would be made to White Haven, Canso, Queensport and Arichat, and were awaiting the arrival of the *Lucy* and *Western Belle* to offer

40

them the charter. Both captains were contacted that day and accepted. Captain Abe agreed to deliver his cargo to the ports of Arichat, on Isle Madame, and Canso, the eastern extremity of the Nova Scotia mainland, while Captain Mose took the Queensport and White Haven consignments.

By four o'clock Tuesday afternoon, the *Western Belle* was sailing southward through the narrow channel separating the ports of Halifax and Dartmouth to the waterfront of Halifax Harbor. All cargo was discharged and she proceeded down the Harbor to the Boake and Bennet Wharf, where the salt cargo would be loaded.

Captain Mose had got rid of the wood, made the call to the oil dock, discharged the empties and beat his rival Abe to it. He already had the *Lucy B.* under the salt chute where Mate Asa Gook was perched comfortably on the wharf tallying the one-half-hogshead barrows of salt that were being dumped down the chute to the cargo hold. Solar salts are the popular salts used in the fishery and vary in weight from six hundred and eighty pounds to almost eight hundred pounds per hogshead. This could either be Turks Island, B.W.I. salt, or Italian Trapini, or African salt from the shores of the Mediterranean, and would roughly average three hogshead per ton. The *Lucy* would carry about two hundred and twenty-five hogshead when trimmed to load-line draught.

Liverpool salt from the United Kingdom is a mineral salt of high quality and free of sea organisms. It is somewhat lighter in weight and by far the best salt for any use, but, having the added cost of production, is more expensive and was only used for choice cure and high-priced fish such as the fat, fall mackerel and sardine herring.

A Visit to the "Bucket of Blood"   Chapter 4

Captain Abe brought the cumbersome *Western Belle* in alongside the Boake and Bennet pier and tied up close astern of the *Lucy B.*, ready to take the next turn under the salt chute. All this activity on board the *Lucy B.* put Captain Abraham on edge. The thought of seeing the *Lucy* get started out on the voyage and leaving him the last to sail was business that had to be taken care of right there and then. He climbed up on the wharf and went in search of friend Mose. Purposely he closed upon the mate to check the amount of salt yet to be loaded on the *Lucy*. He learned from the tally and rate of progress that she would be loaded by ten o'clock next morning, and glancing in an uptown direction saw one of the familiar canvas-covered horse-drawn wagons heading toward the wharf shed. His suspicions were correct — it was Captain Mose standing behind the elevated driver's seat under the front edge of the canvas covering, as the team drew closer to the large shed doors which were opened to the salt chute.

Captain Abe departed along the wharf head approximately one hundred feet, to glance casually about at his own vessel, and at the same time give Captain Mose the privacy he would appreciate to transfer the special packages he had just brought from the liquor export firm. When Mose saw his seaman go down the cabin with the last of the packages, he hailed Captain Abe whom he had been noticing the last few minutes.

"What's the matter, old man, getting frightened of horses?"

"Not so much feared of horses, Captain, as I am of the scent you picks up from being close where they is, particularly when I hope we are going ashore together tonight."

"Got something good lined up, Captain?" queried Mose.

Abe recognized a sharp pitch in the tone of Mose's voice and, noticing a shine in his eye, knew he had sampled the contents from a couple of the vats at the export company.

"Why, yes, Mose, the picture house is showing 'Islands out in the Pacific Ocean.' Heard the talk of it in the Customs House."

"Well, come on board and get a little appetizer before supper."

Abe needed both an appetizer and a bracer as well. Something had to be arranged to prevent the *Lucy B.* from sailing the next day if at all possible, and Abe had to make that arrangement in the next few hours. After a few swigs of Mose's liquor they agreed to be ready and leave for the picture house at seven o'clock.

The big sign-boards at the entrance to the picture house had large paper posters showing two half-naked and bearded men adrift on a crude raft with pretty, low, flat islands shaded by tall palm trees, and shiny black natives crouching in the tall grass near the beach. The picture was a "silent", with the story coming on the screen in print. The raft floated the two shipwrecked mariners ashore on the cannibal-inhabited island. Little knowing the reception awaiting them, their weakened spirits rose high with the hope of getting on shore to find fresh water and possible food. One section of the picture showed the entrance to a cave where a large iron pot was suspended over a fire-place, all prepared to be put into use. Finally, the raft came aground on the beach, the weakened men dragged the end of a rope over the beach and secured the raft to the base of a small palm, unaware of being surrounded by the cannibals. They immediately commenced a search for water. However, the search was brief because the reception committee closed in, stripped and bound the two, and led them off toward the cave. Fortunately via a route where the cooking pot was not visible. The sound of drums brought the shiny black figures from all directions and they formed up in a wild dance which was cut short by a threatened tropical squall. Heavy black clouds cut out the hot sun, and a gloom came over the island. Smoke suddenly rose nearby and as the shipwrecked pair were rushed toward the large pot at the point of long bamboo poles they realized what was now about to take place, and could see no means of escape. The grass and reed fire was burning furiously around the pot, and the shipwrecked pair were about to be heaved into the steaming water, when all of a sudden, lightning and thunder broke loose with a violent squall of wind. Coconuts were flying in all directions, and two large palms were uprooted on top of the iron pot. The natives made a mad rush for the cave; the shipwrecked men stumbled and crawled for the raft. They just reached it as the tidal wave was taking it off shore; then more thunder, lightning and rain, as the two mariners clung to the raft and drifted away. The picture ended with the last scene showing the two securing more than a dozen coconuts that had fallen on the raft, sufficient to supply drink and food for several days. The lights came on to end the picture show. Abe and Mose got a good laugh out of the event and reckoned, after all, the squall hit the right place at the right time.

Captain Abe had watched the picture but was doing some tall thinking all through, in hopes of devising a scheme of some sort that would delay Mose's sailing next morning. He had an idea and thought by chance it might work. After the exit from the picture house, Captain Abe persuaded Mose to take a walk along through that section of the town where it is much safer after dark to walk the street rather than the poorly lighted sidewalk. After turning a few corners, Mose sighted, dead ahead, a brightly-lighted canopy over a set of large double doors. Over the doorway in the lighted area could be seen a bucket having a bright red splash painted down over the side.

"That's it!" announced Abe. "Best drinks in town."

Mose began to feel a little uncomfortable, but who could give in at this stage? By this time, Abe had thrown his weight against the heavy oak door and pushed it open. The bright lights inside were dimmed through the heavy cigar and pipe smoke. The hum and noise of voices drowned out the chance of a conversation in any normal tone of voice.

The place was crowded with seamen, lumbermen, fishermen, and sailors ashore off a foreign man-o'-war anchored out on the Harbor. Abe and Mose finally reached the long bar and were obliged with prompt service.

"This is my first visit to this section of the City," said Mose.

"Ye mean to tell me you sailed outa this port all these years and never called in to the 'Bucket O' Blood' before?" snickered Abe.

"'Bucket O' Blood'", replied Mose, "had I known it, I wouldn't be caught here now, either."

Abe laughed and nodded to the bartender. The glasses were replenished.

Abe stood up to get some money from his pocket, and noticed, across the large room, a tall metal contraption around which several customers had collected, and nudged Mose.

"Over here!"

Some kind of game was going on. When they got to where they could see, it was a waterfront stevedore, matching his strength against a big man-o'-war sailor. The idea was to grasp two lever bars and pull down against spring tension to turn on a series of colored lights and reach a maximum lift, when bells would ring. The man-o'-war sailor might have been financially handicapped by the money exchange, but drinks and cigars were coming fast and furious each time he topped the stevedore with another colored light. Mose began to enjoy the fun, bought a handful of cigars and set them up for the next try. After seeing the stevedore claim the cigars, Abe set up the drinks for each of the pair and with Mose, retired to a corner table.

Everything was going fine until a smart alec quietly slipped up behind Captain Mose and reached under his arm to steal his drink off the table. As he was about to escape with the drink, Abe's long leg reached out across his trail, caught the culprit's lower leg with his foot and pitched him, head first, over the shoulders and onto the next table which was occupied by four sailors. The four tars picked him up bodily, sang a few bars of a sea shanty as they swayed him back and forth to gain momentum and shot him through the air, feet first, back on top of Captain Mose. They then reached back and upset the table that Mose and Abe were sitting at. This brought the bouncer, followed by the crowd. Lights went out, tables crashed, somebody got the maximum lift on the levers of the weight machine and the bells were ringing. However, eventually the lights came on again, and here and there amongst the crowd could clearly be noticed the shiny blue helmets of City police officers.

Captain Abe cunningly made use of the blackout and slipped up to the bar, clear away from the scene of combat. The bouncer signalled the police constables and they soon closed in on the culprit, Captain Mose, and the four sailors. One police constable commenced making satisfactory identifications and taking names. The smart alec attempted a poke at Captain Mose but lost out to a drive in the paddy wagon, wearing a pair of handcuffs.

The police constable gave Captain Mose and the four sailors written documents instructing them to be present in the City Police Court at eleven o'clock the next day to give evidence concerning the disturbance.

During the return walk from the "Bucket O'Blood" to the schooners, Captain Mose's comments were not too favorable on the evening's events. This tickled Abe, but the poker-faced old skipper expressed sincere regret that it had resulted in his becoming involved with the Law. However, when they arrived on Boake and

Bennet's Wharf, Captain Mose invited Abe on board for a nightcap before turning in, for what was left of the night.

The man-o'-war at anchor in the Harbor maintained an hourly liberty-boat schedule to King's Wharf, and somehow, deliberately or otherwise, it happened that just a few minutes past ten a.m., Captain Abe was walking past the large wooden gate leading from King's Wharf out onto Water Street and the City.

"Bonjour, Capytan! Bonjour Capytan!" came ringing in his ears and in an instant he was circled by the four tars who were being escorted by a naval officer of higher rank, having his sleeves ornamented with large pointed bands of red military lace.

Abe shook hands with them and suggested going for a bracer. The escort made violent signs with his hands which Abe interpreted to mean they were granted fifteen minutes.

Away they all headed to Pat Ryan's Bar. Abe bought the refreshments and insisted that they would not "try to fly on one wing". When they departed from the Bar, Abe knew he had succeeded in holding Captain Mose in Harbor for the day. A half-hour later he learned from Mose that the sailors had gotten lost and arrived late, so the hearing had to be put off until three p.m.

Abe had got through a lot of business that morning. He had the *Western Belle* under the salt chute immediately after the *Lucy B.* was moved, had reported to Customs, the Export Company, and was well outfitted with tobacco and little brown jugs. He returned the compliment of inviting Mose aboard for an appetizer before dinner. Mose made known his determination to sail immediately after the Court hearing and Abe reckoned he would get away about seven o'clock and would make Arichat on Cape Breton Island the first port of call, and Canso Harbor second. Captain Mose announced he would go on to White Haven and then to Queensport. They would not be more than thirty-five miles apart at any time while in port discharging.

Sure enough, at three-thirty Captain Mose returned from the court hearing, freed by the magistrate, not having been required even to give evidence. The mate had the schooner moved out to the end of the pier, mainsail and foresail hoisted, and ready for a quick get-away.

Captain Abe met Mose and walked out to the pier head with him. Captain Mose was dressed in a blue serge suit with a heavy gold watch-chain slung across from vest pocket to vest pocket. He

46

wasted no time in changing over to sea-going togs, but went directly to the steering-wheel and commenced manoeuvering the schooner away from the pier. Abe let the lines go and announced that he would be following along in a few hours time. When the trim *Lucy B.'s* sails filled with the fresh southwest breeze, she soon began to disappear down Harbor.

Abe sized up the loading operations of his own schooner and estimated that he needed at least three more hours to complete the full cargo. This gave him a chance to meander down along the water-front and visit some of the other trading schooners. Some of the Chezzetcook fleet were in on the first trip of the season. The *Agnes* was berthed at one of the larger salt fish firms and was discharging barrels of salted clams. Salted clams were used as bait by the large bank handline fishing schooners and the sand flats of the Chezzetcook and Petpeswick Inlet area produced a great percentage of this shell fish. The natives of these areas dug, shelled, and salted the clams during the fine winter days when the flats were free of ice, and so a supply was always ready for the first trading schooner, for Halifax, Lunenburg or LaHave.

Two schooners were in, and berthed at the Building Supply Wharf unloading Chester sand. The beaches of Chester Bay produce a very high quality sand for use in concrete work, and so Captain Abe spent an interesting two hours talking over the pros and cons of the business with the other captains. Abe's home port was west of Halifax and he was always anxious to take a charter for that area whenever possible.

Captain Abe returned to his schooner for supper, treated the crew to an appetizer and after the meal, got himself hard at work with the crew, battening down the main hatch. That section of the cargo hold was filled and the wooden hatches fitted on. However, with a cargo of salt, the hatches and deck must be watertight, so tarpaulins had to be spread over the hatch, turned down over the edges, and secured tightly to the hatch coamings. The fore hatch was fitted with a scuttle box and was fairly well protected without the "tarps".

The loading gang had worked through the suppertime hour and at six-thirty Captain Abe decided the vessel was deep enough for going to sea, and ordered loading to cease. The plant superintendent came down with the necessary invoices and bills that would require signatures and receipts of delivery. Once Abe had this matter seen to, he got the vessel underway and out on the voyage.

Choppy Water   Chapter 5

The sun was setting in a grey bank and indicated some unsettled weather. The air was humid and the sky becoming overcast. The breeze increased its velocity slightly as the night came on. A south or southwest wind on the Nova Scotia coast can kick up a storm to give any small salt-laden schooner a tough time of it, and with this in mind, Captain Abe showed a wee bit of concern. Once out of the Harbor they had to take what came. Since Abe knew the old schooner to be sound, with good strong sails and ropes, he decided to proceed. This time he stood well out in the fairway rather than taking the close turn at Thrumcap, and at eight-thirty, when the watch brought the red and green port and starboard side-lights up from the forecastle and proceeded to lash them in their board boxes high in the fore-rigging, the bright beam of Chebucto Head light was distinctly showing the mist in the air as it flashed. Close on the port bow was the high-pitched groan of the whistle buoy as it swayed in the choppy sea.

The side-lights for that type of schooner were oil lamps with a cotton wick, and at sunset they would be taken to the forecastle, filled with oil, and the wicks trimmed and lighted. They were then fitted in a groove within a large lantern having a colored shade, and taken up and secured in the light boxes that were so constructed as to prevent the green light from being seen on the port side or the red light from being seen on the starboard side.

On rounding the buoy, Abe set the course ESE (ten degrees farther off shore than was necessary to make a straight course), but they had to be in such a position that should the wind suddenly veer from the south, they could sail on, without tacking, before morning. The sea was choppy now and the decks were continually awash.

A salt cargo is heavy and gives the vessel so much stability that she is unable to rise and roll with the swell, and therefore in choppy water she fights the sea and ships lots of green water. The outer jib

48

was lowered and secured and the main sheet eased slightly. They estimated the speed at eight knots. Two men were alotted hourly watches, one to steer and the other on lookout, for half-hour shifts each. At the end of the hour they would be relieved by the other watch, the captain and mate in turn being in charge of each watch. Sea boots, oil skins and sou'westers were the rig for that sort of weather. Water was a foot deep on the lee side of the deck most of the time, with rain squalls, in addition to the increasing breeze, all the early part of the night. However, at midnight there were signs of improvement: the sky began to clear, and coastal lights could be sighted. Abe got a good bearing of Egg Island Light and with the improvement in weather, he altered course and steered east. This put the schooner in a much easier seaway and as the wind veered from the west and moderated, conditions on board then became more comfortable.

The routine on board the *Lucy B.* paralleled that of the cumbersome *Western Belle*. Captain Mose was worse off in the respect that he was one man short in crew complement, having not found a suitable replacement for Lamoy. At midnight, the smart little *Lucy B.* had ploughed through the choppy water and was off Liscomb Islands. She had covered a distance of more than eighty miles since departing from the Boake and Bennet Wharf in Halifax at four o'clock in the afternoon. Another five hours sailing at this rate, and the *Lucy* would be rounding Tree Top Island and heading up White Haven Harbor.

Captain Mose gave a sigh of relief when his calculations worked out this way. The last twenty-fours hours in Halifax had him more or less "coralled", and turning round in circles. Now he had come out of that state of affairs and would be arriving at the port of call at the very beginning of the work day. He would then be once again a full twenty-four hours ahead of friend Abe. There was no doubt that he would have half his salt cargo discharged and be sailing for Queensport before the *Western Belle* would be arriving at Arichat. The distance from Halifax to Arichat via direct sea route would be roughly one hundred and forty miles and the *Western Belle* had made a good thirty miles by midnight.

When daylight broke, the *Western Belle* and *Nannie O'Hara* were less than one mile apart. The wind had veered and was blowing from a westerly direction at a ten knot velocity. The speed of the schooners had dropped to an estimated six knots. The opening gap between Western Islands and Sheet Rock was shaping up and

49

beginning to show the narrow entrance to Sheet Harbor. Soon the *O'Hara* would alter course and trim sheets to sail up the long narrow western arm of the very picturesque inlet. By nine o'clock, the decks of the *Western Belle* shone in the bright sun with a glistening coat of tiny salt crystals. Having had so much salt sea water washed across the decks during the night, the drying up of the moisture left the powdery white surface shining and cleansed of the smallest grain of dust.

Sailing along the coast just far enough off shore to view both the coastline contour and the elevation of the inland approaches (particularly off the Eastern Shore of Nova Scotia) revealed a wealth of scenery that was never to be forgotten. Sailing eastward along the south east Nova Scotia coastline during the day, you see the bold whitish grey, barren granite cliffs of the shoreline, the green wooded terrain immediately behind, dotted here and there with small fishing villages. Tall, white church spires and brightly painted homes are cosily huddled together around the shores of the many sheltered inlets. The bright sun, from the instant its upper curve comes over the horizon, until it sinks below the western horizon in the evening, shines over your shoulder, down on that shoreline as you sail past, so that every detail of color and contour is brought out and magnified, making the cruise an artist's paradise.

Captain Abe watched the *Nannie O'Hara* round the Sheet Harbor fairway buoy and stand in for the narrow passageway to arrive at her port of call, and went below to his bunk for some well-earned sleep. He had only been below decks long enough to eat and enjoy a few minutes smoke, from the time they left Halifax until daylight, and had good reason to believe he might spend a considerable time up again this night, piloting the schooner clear of the treacherous Cape Canso shoals and reefs. Courses would have to be altered from time to time to round this, the extreme eastern end of the mainland of Nova Scotia, and head north, north eastward up and across Chedabucto Bay and on to where Cape Breton Island and the Nova Scotia peninsula have just missed being one, by the narrow, deep, navigable passageway known as the Strait of Canso.

At sunrise on Thursday morning, when the lightkeeper went to attend to the daily routine of extinguishing the light in the little

50

tower of Tree Top Island lighthouse, he could see the salt-laden *Lucy* heading inward between Black Ledge and Bald Rock to pass through the narrow passageway, only feet away from the base of the lighthouse, and head northerly up bay to Marshall Cove and on with the job of discharging that very much needed salt supply.

Fore-and-aft rigged schooners like the *Western Belle* and *Lucy B.* acted as distributors for ocean going vessels and in turn, smaller craft, usually sloop-rigged, served to take care of local areas and could navigate the more reef-strewn and shallow inlets. Some of these boats were waiting at Marshall Cove for deliveries of the salt cargo which they would disperse locally.

The *Maud G.* escaped the wind storm because of an extra day in port. The variety of small package cargo she was loading came slow, so it was late in the day when Captain Hodson received his bills of lading and was free to get underway for his voyage down the coast. He would head for Queensport and possibly meet Captain Griffin before returning to Halifax.

After the sun had reached the zenith at noon and began losing altitude toward the western horizon, a fresh northwest wind slowly increased from a moderate to a strong breeze, very satisfactory and favorable for the *Western Belle*. By two p.m. that well-known eastern landmark, Cranberry Island Lighthouse at the entrance to Canso Harbor, was four miles on the port beam. This put the schooner in the geographical position for rounding Cape Canso and heading across that large exposed Chedabucto Bay, bounded on the northwest by Nova Scotia and on the northeast by Cape Breton Island. Fourteen miles north from the tip of Canso Cape is the approach to the Strait of Canso and the southwesternmost entrance to the Gulf of St. Lawrence — one of the routes commonly used by ships trading from the British West Indies and South America to Quebec and Montreal, and on into the Great Lakes.

It was April, and rounding Cape Canso bound north was like crossing the Gulf Stream, northbound, in February. The prevailing north wind and strong southerly current brought large fields of Gulf ice out through the Straits, and made Chedabucto Bay an area that had to be navigated with caution. Navigating a sailing vessel, salt laden, under these conditions, it would not be good seamanship to undertake the passage across the bay during the night.

Captain Abe had the choice of sheltering at Canso Harbor (only a couple of miles inside Cranberry Island) or carrying on over a route that would cover fourteen miles, to enter Arichat Harbor. When they rounded the Cape and opened up the approaches of the Bay, Abe climbed aloft on the masthead to get a better view of ice conditions. The wind was blowing hard from a NNW direction. Coming off the ice it made the air cold and clammy. The situation Captain Abe discovered from the masthead showed a considerable amount of drift ice, mostly in the WSW section of the Bay. Clear water was sighted all along the Cape Breton coast and offered a very good chance of clear roundabout sailing and an arrival at safe anchorage, or maybe, in and alongside the wharf at Arichat before nightfall.

Abe came down from aloft, set the course to cross the mouth of the Bay and arrive on the Cape Breton coast at Cape Hogan, the southwesterly tip of Cape Breton Island, not more than four miles from the Arichat Government Wharf.

The passage across the approaches of Chedabucto Bay, from Cape Canso to Cape Hogan, was a wet one for the *Western Belle*. The Bay runs in for a distance of approximately seventeen miles from the entrance, and can be quite choppy when the spring northerly winds blow out through the Straits from the Gulf of St. Lawrence. Several times her decks became so filled with green water that she had to be pointed to the wind, and eased to free herself of the excess weight of water. However, once across, within a mile of the Cape Breton shore, there was shelter and smoother water. Heavy field ice was only a few miles away to the WNW, but as Captain Abe had figured, there was clear passageway close along the shoreline and into Arichat Harbor. The wind was from the right direction and favorable for sailing in through the very narrow entrance. The sun had gone down behind the high hills of Guysborough County, across on the Nova Scotia side of the Bay, long before the schooner arrived at the wharf.

Millwood Jack was a veteran schooner cook, but under these conditions was obliged to keep his pots and pans secured in their bins as well as the forecastle stovepipe secured below deck, and the hole in the deck plate plugged, so they had a late supper that evening. When sails were furled, an oil lantern was hung high enough above the deck to mark the schooner's being berthed at the wharf, also to warn other incoming craft. The captain commanded the crew back to the cabin to fetch their mugs. There was no delay in executing that operation. Abe was wrestling with a little jug and a loose coil of rope when the crew commenced coming down the companionway ladder.

"Ye had him well lashed down, old man," joked Rube Zinck.

"Well, I has the patience to undo the lashin's, more than I expect ye give the lashin's on them mugs. I reckon the cupboard door must be torn right off, only way ye could all be here so soon."

He passed the jug to the cook, "You first, Jack, fill her up and get busy with some vittles, that cold air makes me terrible hungry."

The contents of the little brown jug took a beating, just as the captain wished. Each man carried a fourteen ounce mug, three-quarters full of the finest grog — appetizers; nightcaps; and one for the morning — all the long evening to enjoy it and celebrate the end of a choppy voyage.

When Captain Griffin saw the mooring lines of the *Lucy B.* all secure, and the schooner berthed in the correct location so as to swing the salt tub in the doorway of the shed, he went below for breakfast. The clock still had ten minutes to go before striking six bells (seven a.m.). Mose figured the route they came would cover approximately one hundred and ten miles during the fourteen hours and thirty minutes under sail — a little better than a seven knot average for the passage.

After breakfast the laborsome operation of discharging the salt cargo commenced. Extra men were supplied from the fish plant: three in the hold, shovelling the bulk salt into two hardwood tubs, with a capacity each of two bushels. The tub was then hoisted out of the hold and up to a level that would allow it to be swung in over the jetty and dumped in a high two-wheel cart for transportation to the salt storage section of the shed. When we stop to think that the entire operation of discharging this heavy cargo had to be accomplished by human brawn and muscle, the rig is well worth describing. A boom, similar in design to the foresail gaff, was shipped on the foremast and hoisted aloft on the mast by using the peak and throat halyards. Special care was given to have the jaws well coated with tallow and fish oil so that it would swing as required with a minimum of resistance. It was the mate's duty to locate the boom correctly so that one pulley block would be directly over the cargo hatch, in order to lift the salt-laden tub perpendicular to the level of the cart at the shed door. The lift rope would then have to lead in to a second pulley block suspended from the under section of the gaff jaws, then downward through a third block on deck, and thence to the horizontal barrel section of the wood constructed hand-operated winch. The revolving of the barrel wound up the lift rope and hoisted the tub aloft, suspending it while the free-swinging boom carried it over to the shed door.

When Captain Mose saw the operation satisfactorily underway, he climbed ashore and off to attend to other items of business. First the routine of visiting the Harbor Master. Fortunately, even from the early days, some official of the Marine Department of the Canadian Government had the foresight to appoint such men as Harbor Masters and Port Wardens at various harbors and areas on the coast. It was their responsibility to keep a record of shipping arrivals, departures, vessel's name, owner and tonnage and Port of Registry, nature of the voyage and details of the cargo; also to register new vessels as they were built and commissioned. Much of that information is still available today and it is interesting and gratifying to know that the National Archives in Ottawa can confirm the names and details of many famous little schooners that played a noble part in early trade and commerce along the coast of our Maritime Provinces.

And now, back with Mose as he called on that respected old gentleman, whose age and physical condition had retired him from the rugged life of the fishing fleet, and who was now in possession of the large heavily bound ledger, iron date stamp, and receipt forms; the instruments of office that made him Port Warden. The captain presented the schooner's registration papers, produced a copy of the manifest and the token fee required to help defray the expenses involved in entry and departure formalities. The old gentleman made a signature on the flimsy receipt form, branded it with the clumsy iron stamp, folded it with the registration papers and passed it back to the captain.

Mose shook hands with the Warden and proceeded to leave but before reaching the door he heard the voice calling,

"Come back, young feller, you're forgetting a parcel."

Mose turned with a friendly smile, "I believe that's for you, sir, if you don't mind."

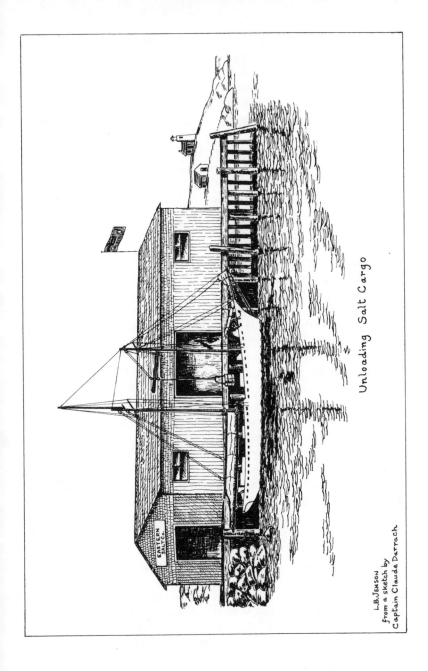

Unloading Salt Cargo

L.B.JENSON
from a sketch by
Captain Claude Darrach

"For me, it is? Well, God bless you, Captain, and may ye always have fair winds and good cargoes."

Mose had only gone a short distance from the Warden's residence when he was hailed by a middle aged man.

"You're Captain Griffin, sir?"

"Supposed to be, my friend," was the prompt reply, "And what can I do for you?"

Mose made the mistake of staring the man in the face as he talked and was obliged to wait a wee bit longer for a reply.

"Th'-th'-th' mate says you want to hire a cook."

Captain Mose turned his glance away from the fellow and enquired what cooking experience he had had on board small schooners. There was no delay this time —

"Have been second cook on the Island Packing Company's boat from the Straits for five years, Captain, but the 'lection last fall changed things for me."

"Well, if you want a job cooking you can start in right now," came the reply, "and I assure you, the election won't interfere but if you're extravagant, dirty, or can't cook, ashore you go!"

"I'll be glad to come, Captain, and with your permission I'll prepare the evening meal today."

"The mate tole you what the wages are?"

"Yes, sir, I understand it's a good average wage."

"You didn't tell me your name yet?"

"Munroe — Jerry Munroe, it is, sir."

"Very well then, we'll see you later, Munroe."

Captain Mose made his next call at the office of the fish plant and found the manager working on a large ledger. The activity of the season was about to commence in a matter of weeks and it was important for the manager to have an up-to-date list of credit ratings for ready reference. They shook hands, discussed the weather conditions and prospects of getting the salt consignment discharged before a rainstorm set in. Mose suggested that the manager should stow the bookwork for the morning, come along with him to the schooner and go óver the manifest and cargo invoices. Mose was as pleased to have someone join him in an appetizer as the manager was to partake of the captain's hospitality. Mose produced one of his specials with the sprig of heather across the label and soon had the big boss in a mood where he had forgotten ledgers and accounts and was telling of experiences out on the sand-flats, shooting wild geese with a new double-barrel, breach-loading shotgun he had purchased while on a visit to Halifax the previous fall. It is not the easiest thing in the world for a sailing skipper to get interested in double-barrel guns, and many close calls some amateur hunters have when shooting down the front column of a flock of wild geese or black ducks.

Just about the time Mose got to changing the subject, Duggan Tanner came to the companionway and informed him dinner was ready. The news of dinner was music to his ears and without delay he shouted for Tanner to join them for a moment.

"Who was the cook, Tanner?"

"There was no cook, Captain, but I made the dinner as it is." Tanner gave a slight cough as he placed the tumbler in its rack, thanked the captain and informed him there was sufficient to invite his guest.

Tanner had tried his hand at a curry and rice dinner and made a very good job of it — fresh beef, diced and garnished with curried gravy, boiled rice and a "duff" for dessert. Duff is the name given to a pudding made from a mixture of light dough, raisins and spices, wrapped in a cotton cloth and boiled in a large pot of water — just the sort of food required for hard-working people. Captain Mose had faith in Tanner's ability to prepare a good meal and felt quite safe in inviting the manager of the plant to have dinner with them. It paid off well because Mose was successful in persuading the boss to hire extra help to speed up the unloading operations.

Ice Bound

Chapter 6

Friday morning at dawn, Captain Abe and Mate Publicover were at work taking the tarpaulin off the hatches to be ready for unloading the salt. Most of the inhabitants of Arichat are bilingual but speak the French language in their every day life. They are Acadians, French both in language and habit — very lovable people, who enjoy good entertainment. The sight of the *Western Belle* was good for them; it meant the first real sign of spring to know that a sailing vessel had made a passage in through the ice.

At six bells, the cook blew the whistle and called all hands to breakfast. Before they had finished the meal a tall heavy-set man descended the ladder, and down in the forecastle he approached the burly looking Abe as he sat in the armchair at the after end of the table.

"You are Capitan Young, sir?"

Abe only had time to nod the affirmative when the man went on to introduce himself as Charles Degou, the wharf boss of the fish plant.

"Oh, good morning, Mr. Gedoo," said the captain. "Will you have some breakfast, sir?"

"Non, non, Capitan, merci, merci. Capitan, you will please move the vessel over to the plant wharf. The water, she is plenty deep there."

"You must be a good pilot in this harbor, Mr. Gedoo. Sure you won't put us on the rocks?"

"Non, non, Capitan, plenty water!"

"Have you got lots of men to help unload the salt, Mr. Gedoo?"

"Wee, wee, Capitan, we get plenty mens."

"Very good then, my friend, we will get moving at once."

To avoid the extra work of hoisting and lowering sails, a small manila rope was strung from the schooner, for a distance of one hundred and fifty yards, to the plant wharf, and the vessel was pulled over from one wharf to the other by use of the crude

58

cargo-hoisting winch. On arrival at the plant wharf the operation of unloading salt commenced without delay, with plenty men on hand to do the job. When Abe saw that things were well underway and going satisfactorily, he called out to Mr. Degou to come on board and see the bills of lading and attend to the signature business.

Once down in the cabin, Abe remarked to his friend that he looked very cold up on the wharf and thought it was time he "better have a little snort". Mr. Degou got a pleasant surprise when Abe came up with the little jug and a couple of tumblers. The closest Mr. Degou got to seeing any bills of lading was when Abe opened his sea chest and got the brown folder containing the vessel's register and clearance papers from Halifax. He was quite proud of the folder and thought how considerate the old Customs Officer at Halifax had been to supply it. Abe made sure that "Mr. Gedoo," as he addressed the man, had a warmer look now and announced that he must proceed to the Customs Officer and officially report the schooner's arrival in port.

The folder fitted snugly in the hip pocket of Abe's homespun trousers. He found stowage in the inside pocket of his suit coat jacket for a slab of Master Mason Smoking Tobacco, checked to be sure he had some money in his pocket, and started off up town to visit the Customs and Harbor Master's Office. The town of Arichat was proud of its Court House that housed the offices of Customs, Law Courts, Post Office, Tax Office, and Fisheries and took care of the business of Isle Madame and Richmond County. The official was quite busy when Abe reported to his office and could not afford time for the usual gossip that skippers and small town officials often get involved in.

As Abe left the building, he found himself amongst a group of men standing near the entrance, chatting leisurely, and with the appearance that they didn't have a worry in the world. He recognized them as being old retired seamen and lumbermen who had been making the routine visit to the post office to pick up the mail. He noticed that one chap carried a bundle of newspapers from Gloucester, Massachusetts, where no doubt he had sailed for several years as a doryman in the famous Gloucester fishing fleet. Two were retired coal miners from the well-known Sydney coal mine district, and the others had never been away from Arichat.

Pedestrians rounding that corner for the next half-hour were obliged to detour to the centre of the roadway. Abe told the boys a couple of favourite yarns of his and heard a few in return. This also gave him a chance to rid his pocket of the overload of tobacco. He passed that over to the old Gloucesterman, addressing him as "Yank" and suggesting he share the chunk among the gang. Both the title of "Yank" and the gift of tobacco went over well and got Abe a special invitation to a "forty-five" card game that evening. Hand-knitted woollen socks and mittens were the items to be played for in the back rooms of Maurice's grocery shop. "Come early for a seat, Capitan," one old fellow advised.

Yank lived in the same direction in which Abe went, on returning to the schooner, and they both jogged along together as the noon meal-hour approached.

Captain Abe stood on the hillside and surveyed the situation out on the bay. The wind was moderate and from the east, packing the ice along the Nova Scotia shore of Chedabucto Bay, blocking off entirely any chance of getting to Queensport. This set his mind thinking of rival Mose. By now the White Haven consignment would be unloaded and the *Lucy B.* would be making the passage down around Cape Canso and up the bay to Queensport, but the existing circumstances regarding ice conditions were going to give Captain Mose a problem. He would not see any ice until off Cape Canso and in the approaches of Chedabucto Bay. Then he would come face to face with an entirely different state of affairs, when he would necessarily have to decide on making shelter at Canso Harbor or proceeding to Arichat and waiting for a west wind, to clear the entrance to Queensport.

Canso would be to the best advantage, providing the harbor was not already blocked. It was too far away for Abe to see, but he was sure it could very well be, particularly with an east wind. In that case there was the chance that the *Lucy B.* might follow the same route as the *Western Belle* and probably spend a day or so in Arichat before getting to Queensport.

After dinner Abe watched the operation of discharging the salt, occasionally glancing out over the southern horizon for a sight of a schooner. The day was fine and sunny with a slowly increasing easterly breeze. When Abe arrived down the forecastle about four p.m. to get a basin of hot water, Millwood Jack dared the remark that he reckoned the old man was "going gallivanting" tonight. Old Abe was noncommittal and only came back to ask the cook whatever gave him that notion. But sure enough when the captain returned to the forecastle for supper, he was wearing his brand-new homespun trousers, a "gansey frock" (a V-necked woollen jersey), a tunic coat, and a brand-new melton cloth bib-cap. After supper he had a short conference with Mate Publicover and went ashore.

He was leisurely walking in the direction he figured Maurice's store to be when two of the old boys overtook him.

"Dat is you, Capitan? All ready for the game?"

Abe recognized the voices and replied in the affirmative. "Hope we are not too late."

"Non, non, Capitan, you will have the game. Non worry!"

Around the bend in the roadway, the illumination of the oil-lamp in the large front shop window lighted up the road.

"The light, Capitan, she is Maurice's place."

"My fren here is Louis Martell, and me is Joe Chaisson, Capitan!"

"Joe and Louis. Well, it's too late to shake on it, boys, knowing we have already met, but before we get in that bright light, let's affirm our friendship with a wee snort."

Abe reached back to the hip pocket of the new homespuns, produced a flask and proceeded to affirm the friendship. They each had a good swig and began the operation of filling their pipes. Joe had a well-seasoned T.D. which he handled quite carefully. He, being the last to light up, was also the last to line up for the second swig.

"There now; friends, the three of us, and flying on both wings, heading for new socks."

Louis gave him a couple of tips on the style of the game, which proved useful to the skipper during the evening. As they entered the shop, they saw "Yank" and some others entering the backroom. They only took time to introduce Captain Young to Maurice, and then ushered him on to the game. Joe was a bit emotional, and now, having both wings spread, had already reached the back room, and reserved a nail keg seat at the table for Abe.

"Eight hands we plays, Capitan; you know that game, yes?"

"Oh yes, often plays eight hands, for old hens and ducks, up along our shore".

It did not take long before sixteen professional "forty-five" card players could be rounded up. The back stowage-room of the grocery store had two kerosene oil-lamps hanging from the ceiling, so arranged that under each lamp a table of eight players could be established. The tables were made up of two battens laid on the top of an empty tea-chest. The seats consisted of empty soap boxes,

61

biscuit boxes, or nail-kegs. Abe got to the table with Martell, and the postmaster, and five more of the town's top-ranking card players. Yank got in at the other table. The eight players were divided into two sets of opposite partners through a means of casting Jacks. Anyone of the eight players would take the deck of cards, shuffle them, and pass them along for another player to cast for partners by dealing out the cards face up one at a time in front of each player, until the four Jacks were exposed. This divided the eight into two teams of four. The two red Jacks sat on opposite sides of the table, face to face, and the two black Jacks opposite, and face to face. This put the four players without Jacks between each of the four with Jacks and made every second man a partner. The honour of getting the first Jack cast demanded the first shuffle and the privilege of deciding the number of games to be played for each prize. At Abe's table, this honour fell to the postmaster.

There was a lot of hidden concern about Abe's ability to play the game, particularly with the three partners in the cast. He drew the Jack of diamonds and as they later found out, Captain Abe could play forty-fives "just as good as the next one". But his handicap was not being able to speak or understand French. One of the younger of the opposite team at Abe's table, a chap named Sampson, caused the skipper the most concern. He was quick to play, could argue a point with a player in French, translate the argument in English for Abe, and all before the defendant had time to make his point or get in his ten cents worth.

The postmaster shuffled the cards, threw them on the table to be cut by the man on his left, and announced five games:

"For dee butt, wee, wee?"

"Wee, wee, dee butt," came back from everybody.

"Me, wee too," said Abe, "but tell me more about the butt."

Sampson explained: "One pair sock for first side to win five game, then all over again, one other pair sock for first five game; then if your side have one win and other side have one win, put she two pair sock up for first five game. That way she eliminate four player and black Jacks and red Jacks play sudden death game. So two mens get pair sock him."

Abe laughed and agreed; he understood. At this point, each man came up with twenty-five cents to cover the cost of the pair of socks, and on went the game.

After a few deals round, they were content that Captain Young could play the game, and one old chap remarked:

"I guess you play pretty much card, Capitan."

"Why, yes, sir! Play a lot when at home in the wintertime. Won half a cow once last fall."

"Half she cow, Capitan?" queried the old man. "How you did that, Capitan?"

Abe replied that he and his playing-mate took half each. The game at this point was getting quite competitive, and the old man only replied in a less interested tone to say,

"Den you win him dead, Capitan?"

Martell was one of the more excitable types of player and was wearing a heavy home-knitted wool cap that he was gradually pushing back more on his neck than head, and an oversized suit coat, which almost reached the floor from the soap-box he sat on. Three deals had gone by since Abe had cunningly transferred an object from the homespun trouser hip-pocket around behind the chap next to him, and deposited it in the side-pocket of Martell's coat. After the hand was played, Martell stood up to adjust the soap-box and discovered the extra weight in his pocket. On investigation, he found a twenty-six ounce flat bottle which he more or less casually extracted from the pocket and held out where everyone could see it.

"She almost full up, too," he said. He pulled the cork and smelled it. They all knew its content by the pleasant expression that came on his face and the demand for the postmaster to "Sniff that, now!"

The old man got a sniff, and made a motion with his hands to keep mum. He went immediately to a bench in the corner where a two-and-one-half gallon pail of drinking water was kept, picked the tin drinking mug off the hook, and returned to the table. A round of drinks was executed in such a manner that the gang at the next table were all unaware of it. No doubt most of the players had a fair idea where the treat came from. The older man commented on the quality and asked Martell, point blank, where he got such fine liquor.

Martell's reply was: "She be dis way, Mr. Chaisson! And, like Fadder O'Rilley say, it must a been the 'leprechauns'."

The man shuffling the deck announced the games four, four and twenty-five, thirty-five, were the points on the last of the fifth game. The dealer, Abe's partner, had to use his five to save the dealing trick. This made the points thirty-five on both sides. The five of trumps counting ten points, the Queen of clubs was led, and the opposite side got that trick. Abe, sitting close to Sampson, noticed that he ignored the club suit and played the deuce of diamonds on the club. Abe's partner got the next trick, to tie the game forty, forty! After taking the trick, he played a club. Sampson hit the table with all five knuckles with the King of clubs. Captain Abe's fist followed with a violent thud, hit the King of clubs with the Jack of clubs, and reminded Sampson in no uncertain terms that his King was dead because it should have been played before, for reneiging suit on the other club lead. Sampson had no choice but to accept, having been caught, and he yielded the trick. And so one pair of socks was won, and the second pair brought up. This called for more twenty-five cent cash-ins.

And on into the second game that could very well result in the opposite side winning, and developing into the butt game. Yank's table took a few minutes longer before the first game was decided and no time was lost getting the second period underway at that table.

Maurice had just opened a barrel of Bishop pippins (one of the Annapolis Valley's famous winter apples) that evening. They were crisp and juicy. They sold for a penny each and it would be a conservative estimate to say the players devoured at least four dozen pippins during the game. Maurice, whenever the opportunity allowed him to get away from a customer, would step inside to watch the game. But only to be dispatched back to the barrel for a couple of pennies worth of apples or maybe a plug of pipe tobacco.

The game never lost tempo until Maurice announced the hour was getting late and the wood-box empty. Abe had gone through the experience of the butt game and came out with two pairs of socks. By this time the air of the storeroom was blue with pipe smoke and nearly everybody was ready to go outside and get some fresh air. Abe bought a half bushel of apples and bargained for several dozen fresh eggs to be delivered on board before he sailed, possibly in two days time. Also, he agreed to freight some empty kerosene oil barrels to Halifax for Maurice, and with the rest of the players, departed for the ship.

Returning on board ship from the card game, the route was over a hill that offered a wide view of the harbor and bay. Abe and Yank were together when they came to this point and Yank being naturally familiar with the local lay of the land was first to notice the anchor lights of two different vessels out in south harbor off Kavanaugh Point and lost no time in pointing them out to Captain

Abe. Almost a mile across the harbor in the background were the lights of the south settlement. Yank for sure, had never counted the number of lights there nor could he make a close estimate of the amount, but having faced the same picture so often was conscious of the two extra lights at first glance. The reflection on the water verified his assumption that two vessels had arrived and were at anchor in the shelter off Kavanaugh Point, not much more than one quarter mile from where the *Western Belle* was berthed.

Captain Abe was not surprised to see at least the one light, because in his bones he felt the *Lucy B.* would have no alternative but to come to Arichat to avoid being caught in the ice field. The second vessel, well, that could be any one of the many schooners that would be operating along the coast. The night was too dark and with the wet haze almost a drizzle, not even a silhouette of the schooners could be sighted.

The hour was late now and Abe looked forward to daylight so as to see and identify, if possible, the two new entries. After watching the two anchor lights for a brief period, they sauntered along the dark roadway, finally arriving at a cross road.

"Now we split tack, Captain," exclaimed Yank. "You find the schooner, you think, Captain?" he queried.

"Oh, I believe, Yank, not very far now!"

"Non, non Capitan, two minute you see the wharfshed."

They bid each other good-night and sure enough, two minutes later Captain Abe sighted the hurricane lantern hanging in the main shrouds of the schooner, and properly arranged in the lighted area was a ladder, secured in such a fashion that it moved up and down with the tide and provided a safe means of boarding the schooner. Abe descended the ladder, walked around the deck, examined the mooring lines, and fenders that prevented the schooner's top sides from rubbing against the wharf piling, found everything ship-shape as he should well have known, and that Mate Publicover had assured himself it would be, before retiring for the night. Abe, like every other good captain, couldn't help this routine. It was "one of those things", and if it served no other purpose, it definitely proved to him he had a reliable mate.

As he put his hand on the companionway slide to push it back, and open the two small doors at the cabin entrance, he could feel the warm, dry air that ascended from the cabin. Millwood Jack, the cook, had lighted the fire in the bogey and banked the hard coal fire. Abe sniffed at the comfortable warm air, its aroma tinted with a mixture of hard coal gas fumes and pine tar coming from the new coil of rope stored in the corner of the cabin.

He entered the cabin, lit the oil lamp that swung in brass gimbals, adjusted the wick to prevent smoking up the clean chimney, and pulled the two pairs of socks from his coat pocket for a closer examination. Grey wool, hand-knit, with a series of red and white strands woven through the top. Abe thrust his big hand into the sock and examined the foot section for knots. Having found an even knitted foot free of knots, he returned his glance to the special woven markings at the top and promised himself to remember the marking and make a special trip to Maurice's place next day to buy a few extra pairs bearing the same pattern of woven strands. A woman that knits a pair of socks without making knots in the feet knows the secret of comfort to a man's foot.

Seldom or ever does a seafaring man turn in for the night without a mug-up. Abe, although having a marked respect for the tired crew that slept in the forecastle, could not resist that trip to the grub locker. A pot of hot tea could always be found on the stove. Abe tip-toed down the long ladder steps to the forecastle deck, eased his way to the cupboard over on the port side, and aft of the bunks.

In the dim light of the forecastle he could see a bulky object on a dish inside the cupboard where the night lunch was kept. On further investigation, the object proved a pleasant surprise when it turned out to be a two pound boiled lobster, fresh caught that day. Up to that time he had avoided making any noise, muttered something to himself to the effect that poached lobsters always had the best flavour, and proceeded to get the meat out of the shell. Nobody ever did get the meat out of lobster claws without making a noise, and neither did Abe. After depositing the empty shells in the garbage bucket, washing and drying the dishes he had used, he went on his way back to the cabin, stopping for a minute on deck to watch the *Lucy's* anchor light.

Cold wet fog coming in off the Atlantic with the easterly breeze prevented any chance of seeing sun or sky after dawn — or even the schooners that were at anchor not more than one quarter of a mile off. Captain Abe was awake and on deck early to satisfy his curiosity about which schooner had arrived the night before, but was disappointed by the fog. However, it was not long after breakfast when a dory was rowed alongside the *Western Belle* and in it were the two Captains, Mose Griffin and Bill Hodson from the *Lucy B.* and the *Maud G.* Abe welcomed them to his vessel and all three proceeded down to the cabin. The story of the previous day's experience manoeuvering around and through the ice field proved the two skippers had had a day of adventure. Each had been off Cape Canso at daylight and met up with the western edge of the ice field, and soon learned that with the support of the easterly wind and current it was setting westward. The ice field was moving at an estimated two miles per hour. The prospect of entering Canso Harbor at that time was dangerous. And so the attempt and hope of skirting the outside edge and finding clear water near the Cape Breton shore was the only possible reason why they should carry on. Otherwise it would be a return westward to shelter again at White Haven.

The moral effect of each having the other in sight must have provided extra courage and so they persisted all day, tacking against easterly wind and adverse current to accomplish a point-to-point distance of eight miles before they dared attempt to make a close approach to the Cape Breton shore and a run for Arichat. It was dark when they sailed in past Cape Hogan, the *Lucy B.* a good mile ahead of the *Maud G.* Both schooners were required to keep all possible sails spread even after dark, to push through the slob ice that fringes along the field, and sometimes packs to a depth of several feet deep. Captain Hodson allowed that at times the little *Maud* had less than a foot of clear water over her keel as she pushed through the slob. Both men agreed it was a wonderful relief to round Marchie Point into the sheltered and clear waters of Arichat Harbor.

Captain Abe announced his consignment would be all discharged in a few hours and he too would be awaiting a chance to proceed on to Canso Harbor, and finish discharging his salt cargo. He was surprised to know that the *Maud G.* also had a charter for Queensport. The three men agreed on expecting the weather conditions to remain unchanged for a few days, much to their disappointment. However, in spite of having very little knowledge of high and low atmospheric pressures, or their effects, these men had instinct and local knowledge that served them well in predicting the weather.

67

Both Captain Abe and Captain Hodson had spent some of their early days going farther afield in small barquentines and brigs in the British West India trade. These ships carried barometers, but seldom or ever did anyone, except the mates and captain, see them. Captain Abe had learned from the mate of one ship how to operate a sextant to get a noon sun sight to determine the latitude. He had more practice than theory of the problem, and so by remembering a simple formula and knowledge to apply the sun's declination to the verticle angle correctly, he could get an estimated latitude position; and that in itself, along with soundings, proved a valuable aid to navigating.

However, it must be remembered that no electronic sounding equipment was available in those days. All the soundings had to be made by hand lead-line. Thus, they were limited both in depth and accuracy. To be a good navigator required the knowledge and ability to take various observations of the sun throughout the day and of certain stars during the night to determine the latitude as well as longitude. This, however, was not necessary in the coasting trade in these small schooners. Good judgement, local knowledge, and pilotage were the required qualifications.

But deep sea or coast-wise navigators were helpless in getting through an ice blockade, and that was the problem which faced the three skippers. Less than ten miles across the Bay, and until a favourable change of wind came, they would remain ice-bound.

All three were so concerned about the situation they were faced with that Captain Abe almost forgot that he was host to the visiting captains. However, he changed the subject by reminding the other two that this occasion, of the three being ice bound together, called for some means of entertainment that would sort of change the luck and melt the ice a bit, and so produced the familiar little jug.

Captain Hodson was a short, heavy-set man and could express a feeling of happiness with a deep, quiet laugh that caused him to shake all over, which needless to say, was his response to Abe's remarks and the presentation of the jug. Millwood Jack knew the two men would be staying for dinner and was glad he had sufficient time to put a few extra frills on the meal — a "Dutch mess," one of Abe's favourites. There are many ways of cooking dried salted codfish, but most people agree on the Dutch mess as tops. Jack had picked a uniform sized supply of potatoes, and carefully peeled and quartered them for cooking. He separated all the bone from the meat of a large, dried, salt cod and flaked and stripped the fish in pieces about the size of a large green bean, then soaked it in fresh water for a few hours. Potatoes and fish were cooked in separate containers. With this the heavy iron fry-pan was put to frying out small diced squares of fat port, rendered and fried until the squares were brought to a dark brown crisp. When the fish and potatoes were cooked, they were placed in a deep bowl in alternate layers, starting with fish at the bottom. Then over the filled bowl were poured the sizzling hot pork scraps so that the fat would filter down through the entire contents. The bowl would then be covered until ready to serve. A duff always went with the Dutch mess menu and so about half an hour before dinner, the cook deposited a white mug in the slack of his white duck apron. He carefully rolled the apron up to the strings, proceeded on deck and back to the Captain's cabin, announced his arrival on the companion ladder, and inquired if there would be company for dinner. Abe understood the language and knew the reason for the bold visit.

"Yer mighty careful to keep that apron clean, cook. Got a furl like a Yankee yacht's jib."

"Ut's not so much the apron, old man, but I been making some sauce for the duff and its a bit too flat to me taste."

"Oh, that's bad, cook," said Abe, "but be sure there's a wee bit gets in the sauce."

Jack made the necessary motions, got the required amount of sauce flavouring, plus a few ounces for good measure, and disappeared up the ladder without effort or delay. Hodson showed a tendency to laugh at the cook's tactics and suggested to Captain Mose they should stay for dinner and get some "Christmas puddin". Abe turned a deaf ear to the remark but was sure they would be having dinner on board, and it was only after another social round that the dinner whistle echoed fore and aft through the old schooner's timbers. The three men came on deck to proceed forward for dinner. They were greeted with increasing wind and rain.

Captain Hodson chirped up a "Ha, ha, and thar she starts. Nothin' like warm rain to melt salt water ice and haul the wind off."

After a hearty dinner enjoyed by all, they retired to the cabin, banked the stove with hard coal and crawled in the cabin bunks for a siesta. Say what you like, but there's no better place to enjoy a good sleep than snugged in the bunk of a wood-constructed schooner. With the rain pattering down on the deck planking not more than two feet above, you can be sound asleep and yet hear every drop strike the deck.

The feeling of protection and comfort that fills the atmosphere of all Bluenose schooner accommodations is a reward to the weary and one of the joys of the seafaring life.

It was the good old ship's clock striking eight bells (4 p.m.) that brought the three back to life again. That, and the absence of the rain patter on the deck. Because when Abe went on deck he was greeted with a sniff of cool, northwesterly wind, and the first sign of what they all needed, a "spring norther", to push the ice off shore to meet the warmer Gulf Stream-affected waters, and as the old sailors say, "sink". Hardly is the term "melt" ever used to describe the disappearance of drift ice. Seriously, we all agree the ice just melts and mixes in with the sea, but ask any old sailor what becomes of the drift ice, and you likely will be told it drifts out to the southward and sinks.

With the clearing weather and increasing northwest wind, both Captain Mose and Captain Hodson decided their place was to be out on board the schooners, particularly when they were swinging to anchor. There's always the danger of fouling the anchor and dragging. And so by midnight the northwest wind had increased to gale force, and both schooners were pulling hard on the anchor chains. Next day both captains rowed ashore again. They joined their friend Abe, and climbed the high hill north of the town where they could watch the ice field from the south entrance of Canso Straits down the bay to Cape Canso and the open sea. The long narrow strait separating mainland Nova Scotia and Cape Breton is the artery through which the Gulf of St. Lawrence ice came through to the Atlantic, but the large bay could not be blocked when the off shore breeze was strong enough to keep the field moving seaward. So it would only be the matter of a day when sufficient open water would permit the schooners a passage across the bay to Queensport and Canso where they could resume the normal routine of loading and discharging cargo.

Not unlike almost every sea-coast village, Arichat displayed a very fine church. It was located high on the hillside overlooking both the village and the sea and it was from this vantage point that the three skippers found themselves watching the ice field and noting that here and there patches of green water were beginning to show as the ice pack broke up. They had spent more than an

70

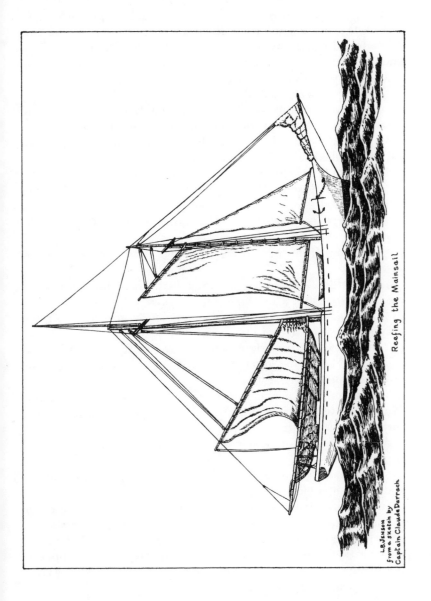

L.B.JENSON
from a sketch by
Captain Claude Darrach

Reefing the Mainsail

hour standing up in the shelter of the large edifice with only one thought in mind: how soon could they get the schooners under sail and venture the voyage across the bay? Would the northwest gale moderate gradually and provide sufficient breeze to carry the little schooners through the scattered ice, or would it flunk out all of a sudden, leave them becalmed, and then come in from a direction that would push the ice-block in again?

Suddenly, in a broad Irish accent, came the words:

"Good morning to ye, my friends," and at first glance they were aware that they had been joined by the parish priest.

Captain Mose was quickest on the draw and got his hand to his cap and replied with a "How do you do, Reverend?"

"Father O'Riley it be, men."

"And I am Mose Griffin," replied Mose with a shake of Father O'Riley's hand.

"This here is Captain Bill Hodson, and here, Captain Abe Young."

"Aha! men from the trading schooners, I bet," came back the priest.

"That's right," said Mose, "but can't do much trading with all this ice in the bay, Father."

"It'll be all gone in a matter of time, men; it goes away off, out o'sight, and sinks, so they say."

"Then it would be alright wit me if the stuff would disappear right now; I had me good share of it, night before last, coming around Cape Hogan."

"Bless your soul, Captain, I dare say it's the truth yer spaking. Must surely be a terrible undertaking to navigate a sailing schooner through the ice fields."

Abe figured it was about enough to watch and wait for the situation to clear up without gabbing about it, and so he broke in on the conversation to tell Father O'Riley he had a mighty fine church and kept it well painted. A compliment to an Irishman is acknowledged in one of two ways,. either with a blessing or an argument, and Abe was honored with the good priest's blessing for good luck and an invitation to see the inside of the church.

"Well, thank you very much, sire, that we'd sure enjoy but maybe not being of the same faith, we'd be a bit awkward and not know what to do as we goes inside."

"Makes no difference what your faith be, men, a church is the place where you show respect for what a church stands for, an' that we learned as kids, and may the Almighty bless all seamen and guide them on their voyages."

It was much warmer inside the large building. The bright sun shining through the stained glass windows, and the beautiful interior church furnishings, took their minds away from the cold wind and ice fields. All four seated themselves in pews, close to a large stove that was designed to burn large chunks of hardwood and proved quite capable of heating the building. Father O'Riley kept the three amused, telling of his bringing up, across the ocean in County Cork, Ireland. Once Mose had to manoeuver on short notice, and give Abe a kick on the ankle to bring him to his senses so that he would put his pipe back in his pocket and not unconsciously put it in his mouth and light it as he was about to do. Father O'Riley, sitting almost back of Abe, never missed a motion, and unbeknown to Abe, saw the move to light the pipe and enjoyed seeing Captain Mose come to the rescue of his friend. With this, the priest announced he had a visiting tour to make before dark and was forced to be getting on his way, and so the three started toward the door and Father O'Riley proceeded to a side room to get his coat and street hat. Outside again, they stopped to size up the weather and were pleased to see several large areas of green water out on the bay, and were assured 'come daylight tomorrow' they would be underway and sailing away from Arichat.

Father O'Riley, although much older than the others, overtook them on the roadway and accompanied them to the wharf to have a close-up view of the *Western Belle*. He was obliged to refuse an invitation to go on board, but allowed Captain Abe to take his black satin bag to the cabin where its contents was increased with a goodly supply of pipe tobacco and a special thought for the old man's birthday, which he had informed them would be next month.

Immediately after Father O'Riley departed, the three men went to the cabin of the *Western Belle*. Jack as usual had the cabin stove well banked with American hard coal. Two bright, red-hot iron cheeks glowed on the bogey, and the aroma of tarred hemp rope ascended the companionway. Captain Abe decided he had better go to the forecastle for a minute, and assured the others it would not be any more than that — not much more anyway; and when he did return he carried a steaming hot jug of water in which floated a slowly dissolving chunk of butter. He set the enamel jug on the stove, reached to the rack and got three glasses, and proceeded to the foot of his bunk where he brought forth the famous little brown jug.

"Now men, make room for some of me 'special mix', called 'Cape Shore Mix'. The finest tonic you can get for this cold spring air, 'specially when it blows off the ice."

Before the first round was over, cunning old Jack invaded the cabin, complained bitterly about the cold, and informed the skipper supper would be ready in about ten minutes time.

"And you put yerself to all that trouble, Cook, to come away back here to let us know. Maybe now ye went and got yerself a chill, coming from that hot forecastle away back here just to 'blige us with 'suppertime'. Too bad ye hadn't thought of ringing the bell. Better have a quick hot toddy afore ye get sick on our hands. Cooks ain't got no time to get sick on board these vessels. No one else can work when stormy weather and ice keeps the schooners in harbor awaiting, early in the morning and late in the night, but the cook still has work to do."

At the same time he was talking, Abe was busy mixing a hot toddy: half a glass of black rum, topped off with steaming hot water, sugar and butter. Old Jack never was in any danger of catching cold, nor did Skipper Abe think so. The cook knew the time was right to gamble on a drink, and Abe was not the one to see him disappointed, and when the cook left the cabin to get back to his work in the forescastle, he carried a sufficient supply for all the men to enjoy a good appetizer before supper.

Bill Hodson and Mose Griffin were anxious to get back to their own vessels out at anchor, for they had high hopes of setting sail at daybreak when the *Maud G.* and the *Lucy B.* would head across Chedabucto Bay for Queensport, and the *Western Belle* out toward the Cape and to Canso Harbor. When the two skippers were about to go on board their schooners, they found themselves face to face with a man wearing the uniform of a Canadian Customs official, who had just boarded the schooner *Western Belle* to interview Captain Abe for any or all the information he could offer regarding the schooners at anchor. This made it quite evident that both masters had overlooked the fact that they should have reported to Customs even though the schooners were at anchor a half-mile out on the bay. Each admitted they had forgotten the Customs, but were under the impression that a Canadian vessel at anchor for shelter only, and not loading or discharging cargo, would be exempt from entering or clearing. It turned out that they both were more alarmed than the officer was concerned. The important point for the officer was to get a record of all shipping that passed in and out of the port and he was quite content to let them go without too much detail. However, the two skippers insisted he go out on board with them and collect the regular port fee, which would give them the privilege of using the harbor until the end of the fiscal year, without additional charge.

As the dory pushed off from alongside the schooner, and headed out to the *Lucy B.* and *Maud G.*, Captain Abe announced that after supper he would be moving out to the anchorage also, to be ready for an early departure. It's much simpler to get a sailing vessel underway and moving from anchorage than from alongside a pier. And so, after all had eaten heartily of Jack's fish cakes and hashed potatoes, the lines were taken in, the main and foresail hoisted, and the schooner gradually eased away from the wharf a safe distance, to hoist the jumbo, and pick up headway on a southeasterly course, and proceed to the entrance of the harbor. Only two sails were lowered, the foresail and jumbo. The main was sheeted in taut and caused the vessel to point directly into the wind and slowly come to a stop. At this, the anchor was let go and chain was paid out, as the schooner slowly drifted stern first. When approximately four times as much chain as the depth of water had been paid out, extra turns were taken over the windlass and nigger head. The stern motion of the vessel caused the anchor to be dragged over the bottom but only far enough to cause the flukes to dig in and bring the schooner to a stop. In this position she would remain pointing in the wind and riding easily on the anchor. The sun was going down behind the western land and the mate brought a lighted hurricane lantern and hung it from the jumbo stay, approximately twelve feet above the deck; a position from which it would show a light all around the horizon and which would be understood by other vessels to be a vessel at anchor, which must be kept clear of.

Anchors Aweigh Chapter 7

During the night the fresh NW breeze moderated and veered to NNW. The course from Arichat to Queensport being west southwesterly, this meant both the *Maud G.* and the *Lucy B.* would be close hauled. The *Western Belle,* bound for Canso Harbour, would head out south and have fair wind. Fourteen miles from port to port would be the approximate distance the *Lucy* and *Maud* would have to sail.

Daylight the next morning found Captain Abe Young climbing high in the rigging, almost to the mast-head, so that he could get all the possible view of the bay he required to make the decision to attempt the passage and avoid being caught in the ice-field. What he saw satisfied him. The chance was good and when he returned down on deck, he ordered the foresail hoisted and the anchor weighed. The crew were weary of lying idle and put every effort into getting the sails set and the anchor hove up in record time. The activity on the other vessels that were less than one hundred yards away was equal to that on board the *Western Belle,* and in less than one hour the three schooners were leading out from Arichat. The *Lucy B.* was setting a pace that neither the *Western Belle* or the *Maude G.* could keep up. It was the *Lucy's* day, with fresh breeze and smooth water. The little *Maud G.* had every inch of canvas pulling, and with a white wave rolling off the bluff bows looked as proud and determined as the two larger craft. The *Western Belle* was running with sheets off and heading out toward a field of scattered ice. The more westerly course to Queensport was practically free of ice except for the odd large pan that could be avoided by keeping a good lookout. To strike hard into a solid ice pan can do serious damage to a wooden hull. To get water leaking in through the seams of a salt-laden vessel is a serious situation. Salt will follow a stream of water through the smallest passage and it is only a matter of time until the pumps are clogged. So to avoid over-strain on a salt laden vessel in open ice-free waters is sometimes very difficult; but to face the added risk of manoeuvering through heavy ice calls for seamanship and courage.

Captain Abe had the shortest distance of only ten miles from Jerseyman Island to Canso, but it was by far the most hazardous. The northwest wind had kept the ice down on that section of the bay shore and the closer the *Western Belle* got to the northern entrance of Canso, the more her skipper had reason to be concerned. When only two miles off Hart's Island Lighthouse, the schooner was rubbing sides with some large chunks of ice. It was not hard, sharp-edged ice, because it had once been solid and covered with snow, but it had broken up, 'way up in the Gulf of St. Lawrence, and drifted for miles. It was wet and slush-like at the edges. Abe had given particular attention to that point and found that he could risk letting the schooner rub hard against the occasional large pan. A glance at any map, plan or navigational chart for that area will show Canso at the extreme easternpoint of the Nova Scotia mainland. Being geographically so situated, it was in a very small way similar to Cape Horn when related to the business of sailing vessels entering or rounding the Cape. It was through a combination of local knowledge and seamanship that Skipper Abe made the decision to risk his vessel and cargo sailing through the drift ice via an unmarked, crooked channel to Canso Harbour.

The outer jib was lowered and furled on the bowsprit when one mile off shore and the halyard ropes were taken off the fife rail posts and placed in readiness to let the sails be lowered on instant notice. The port anchor was made ready to slip, with sufficient chain ranged over the forepeak deck to reach bottom. Bill Publicover, the mate, stood at the wheel steering, and Skipper Abe climbed to the sheer pole of the windward fore-rigging and gave orders "Luff', or "Keep off', as required, both to clear the ice clampers, and at times avoid shallow water where sunken rocks would tear the bottom off the craft.

The direction, or course to steer in, via the north entrance, was first southerly, gradually curving toward the westward, indicating that a west wind would blow out from the inner harbour. Abe's local knowledge made him aware of that and the fact that smoke from the tall fertilizer factory chimney was definitely going out over the harbour, gave him assurance that the inner harbour would be ice-free and that the fringe ice up to one-half mile offshore, would not be packed solid enough to interfere with steering the course required to keep the channel. Abe conned the schooner until, about three-quarters of a mile off Hart's Island, the north range light beacon in Canso town and the lighthouse on Hart's Island were in line. He then ordered course S$\frac{1}{4}$W and the vessel sailed in past the dangerous net rocks. Less than two hundred feet off the starboard side, he noticed a large junk of ice grounded on the rock. The passage between Hart's Island and Piscatiqui Island is less than two hundred feet wide at low tide and now it was through this passage that *Western Belle* was about to go. Should it suddenly appear that ice had the passage blocked, the only manoeuver to avoid disaster was to let the sails be lowered away instantly and at random, and at the same moment, drop the anchor, and hope that the suden jerk on the chain cable would stand the strain to bring the vessel to.

It proved that Abe's assumption of the westerly wind was correct and it had cleared the harbour. The narrow passage was made without a hitch. The skipper, much more relaxed now, came down on deck and went back to take over the wheel for the short distance up harbour to the wharf. Their position now gave them time for a brief glance westward along the eastern coast on the route toward Halifax. In that direction and not more than two miles away, the wind was blowing from the southwest, with much more force than that of the north-northwest wind just around the corner and in the bay — thus the slight similarity to the conditions encountered by the large sailing ships making passage around Cape Horn, at the southern tip of South America.

Soon after Abe had taken the wheel, the sheets had to be trimmed in and it was necessary to make two short tacks to windward to fetch in and come alongside at the Whitman & Company Wharf. More than fifty (mostly waterfront) people were on the wharf to see the schooner berth and welcome the skipper and crew in port. The skipper checked the time and found he still had plenty to get to the Customs House and go through the formalities of reporting before twelve o'clock. He was quite proud of himself for having the worry of the trip across the ice-covered bay behind him, and was now ready to proceed on another adventure.

Like the people at Canso, standing at vantage points to watch the *Western Belle* arrive in port, so the Queensport people watched the *Lucy B.* and the *Maud G.* as they headed across the bay and neared the Rook Island passage to berth in the sheltered harbour. The *Lucy* had more than two miles lead on the *Maud* now and would fetch to windward of Rook Island to swing off and run down harbour to the fish plant wharf. The *Maud G.* had made more leeway on the passage over, and would have to tack and stand off again before fetching to windward of the Island.

Cape Canso, extending well out in the north Atlantic Ocean, was wind-swept, barren and rocky, and served only as a fishing port. So Captain Abe was among people that knew the sea and lived as seamen do. Many of them spent months at a time away from home as crew men on board the Gloucester halibuters or the Lunenburg salt bankers and it was common for one of the long, black, lofty schooners of Lunenburg or Gloucester to call at Canso for fresh bait and have three or four Canso men in the crew. This would be an outstanding event and would call for a party ashore. American tobacco and cigarettes were a particular treat and the boys commuting ashore for an evening were usually sufficiently stocked to stand a goodly handout.

However, the *Western Belle* was not a fishing schooner; but her mission to Canso was a very important one. She carried the necessary supply of fishery salt required to preserve the spring catch of codfish. Now that the ice had started to disappear and permit navigation, so too would the fishing begin, and the spring run of cod had a lot to do with the economic situation of both fishermen and fish handlers at the shore plants.

It was Saturday now and Abe became aware of that for the first time that day when he walked into the Customs House and saw the large date pad hanging over the clerk's desk. Waiting for fog and ice to clear away, he had concentrated more on weather and ice conditions than on the passage of time. However, when he did return to the vessel, he was pleased to see that the hatches were off and that men were standing by with two-wheeled carts and ready to commence discharging the salt cargo at one o'clock.

Canso's geographical position also made it a very suitable point for some trans-ocean telegraph cable to come ashore, and so, to accommodate the landing and transmitting of cable communications, the town boasted an electric power-generating plant, receiving and transmitting buildings, telegraph offices and staff houses. This was in many ways an asset to the town and brought in people who were of social benefit to the community as a whole.

When the factory whistle sounded the long, shrill blast (the signal to turn to for the afternoon shift) salt shovels went into action in the cargo hold of the *Western Belle* and from then until five o'clock, tub after tub of clear, white salt crystals were hoisted up from the hold, dumped into carts and wheeled to the salt-shed. Captain Abe had spent the afternoon conversing with the people coming down on the wharf and some he met up-town when he walked to the post office and checked the general delivery for any mail addressed to the *Western Belle*. Sure enough, there were letters for Mate Publicover and Caleb Madera. He was also fortunate enough to get some Halifax newspapers only a few days old. Saturday night offered nothing exciting ashore, and when Abe returned to the schooner, just before six o'clock, he had definitely made up his mind to retire for the night. Hatches were closed and covered with canvas tarpaulins, and supper was waiting the old man's arrival. Abe was not surprised when he went to the forecastle for supper and saw the going-ashore togs being taken from the suitcases and hung out to dispose of the suitcase folds and wrinkles, and noted the aroma of scented shaving soap. All this automatically informed him that, for sure, he would be keeping ship tonight.

"Well," thought Abe to himself, "good luck to them. Don't believe they had one night ashore since leaving Halifax, and this will do 'em good, to get their feet on the soil again for a few hours."

Before Skipper Abe left the forecastle supper table, he reached in his trouser pocket and came out with a fold of paper bank notes, from which he found enough two dollar bills to pass to each man of the crew. The fact that this casual gift had not been requested, and the manner in which Abe had dished out the cash, assured the crewmen it was a gesture of good will, and would not be deducted from the monthly wages.

When the captain returned to his cabin and squared away in his easy chair, it just occurred to him that he had been wearing his boots since four-thirty that morning, and had not had a wink of sleep all day. So, the bunk for him now.

The illumination from the red-hot coals of the hard coal fire in the cabin stove supplied all the necessary light Abe needed to get off most of his clothes and crawl in the bunk. The fresh southwest breeze increased slightly after sunset and the only sound that Abe could hear above the peace and quietness of his cabin resort was an occasional shower of sand dust which a little gust of wind would collect and blow off the wharf to fall on the deck over where Abe was resting. Suddenly the tiny sand storms had no more effect on Abe's thoughts — he was asleep: tired, and enjoying the comfort and rest of a mohair mattress, on plain boards without a spring, lots of heat and fresh air, and at peace with the world. As the ship's clock struck six bells, Millwood Jack tip-toed down the companion-way and checked the fire, saw that the skipper was clewed up for the evening and returned up on deck without making even as much noise as the tiny sand-storms that had lulled the captain to sleep.

Meandering Ashore

Zinck, Publicover and Madera were waiting up on the wharf when Jack returned on deck to join them for an evening's meandering. Each commented on the appearance of the others' dress clothes and the manner in which they stood up to being stowed in a leather suitcase for so long.

The first stop was at the drug store. Mate Publicover bought a cake of camphor-ice, his favorite hand lotion; Madera picked out a heavy briar pipe with circular tapered bowl and flat mouthpiece, and Zinck bought some soap. By this time, Jack complained that the pretty smell of the drug store was too much for him, and he must get out in the fresh air.

They strolled a couple of blocks farther up town when Jack sighted a dry goods store, "Nick's Supply House." He was the first to enter the store and get down to shopping, finding a black satin shirt just his size and at a price that he could accept. He also bought two new dish cloths, handkerchiefs, some thread and needles. The other three indulged only in window shopping, and were attracted by small groups of people entering a large building just a short distance up the street. When Jack had made his exit, with a bundle under his arm, they were proceeding to investigate the attraction, when they suddenly were overtaken by two lassies in the uniform which is recognized the world over. Their curiosity was satisfied. It was the Salvation Army Hostel, and the three agreed then just how the balance of the evening would be spent.

It was warm and cheerful inside; books and papers to read; pen, paper and even stamps for visitors in need of them, and anxious to write and mail a letter. They lined up at the large Visitors' Register and Madera had the honor of entering the three names and home addresses in the large book. People continued to arrive until the room was almost filled to capacity. Some women carried bundles and went to a kitchen off the large room. Hours of pleasant entertainment soon pass, and such was the case for the men ashore from the *Western Belle*. They had enjoyed music, song and refreshments, and as the illuminated clock in the post office tower ticked off the hour of eleven, they were on the return route to the schooner.

Arriving on board, Mate Publicover proceeded to the cabin and deliberately made sufficient noise to awaken the captain, and present him with a bundle of newspapers, the *Daily Echo*, that famous Grit publication from Halifax noted for its special pages on coastal and foreign shipping. Captain Abe, in a semi-conscious condition after the sound sleep, was out of the bunk and standing near the companionway where the fresh air gradually awakened him to his right senses; then he inquired of Publicover what brought him to the cabin, and if the others had returned safe or were locked up in the Town Jail. Publicover's gruff reply was that there was no danger of any of the forecastle's gang getting in jail, which more or less insinuated that the skipper himself should have regard for the possibility of becoming the guest of the Town, and went on to inform him that they had enjoyed a nice evening at the Salvation Army meeting and the newspapers were with the compliments of the Army captain.

Without noise, warning or effort, fleet-footed Millwood Jack presented himself in the cabin and commenced the operation of fixing the hard-coal fire in the cabin stove so that it would continue buring at a moderate rate until the next morning. Jack paid no attention whatever to the other two men. He completed the job of replenishing the stove with coal, adjusted the drafts and dampers, focussed his glance directly on Abe and announced that the bean-crock was in the oven and a fresh pot of tea had been made. Then, just as effortlessly as he had arrived, he made his exit up the companionway and to the forecastle.

The captain and mate conversed mainly on the business of discharging the salt cargo and cleaning and drying out the hold to take on another load of freight — the business Abe had facing him now was to procure another charter. At this point, the habit of mugging-up got the best of him and a few minutes later he was in the forecastle helping himself to a goodly portion of baked beans and fresh buns. After this he returned to his cabin and spent the wee hours of the morning reading the Halifax newspapers. One item of interest was an article on the marine pages announcing that the new government pier at Sheet Harbour was completed and that the three-masted schooner, *Lady McKeen,* was berthed there loading lumber for New York. This meant that the *Nannie O'Hara* would have ended the contract of carrying wharf building materials to that port, and would be back at the regular coastal trading of the general cargo type.

The arrival of *Lucy B.* and *Maud G.* at Queensport started a scene of activity at two locations. The men at the cannery across on the east side worked through until late at night unloading the stores from the *Maud G.* and, over near the bridge where the *Lucy B.* was berthed at the M. & S. Fisheries, salt was being unloaded until dark. That evening every one was conscious of the fact that with the disappearance of the ice, fishing operations would commence immediately.

Sunday at both Queensport and Canso, particularly at this season, was a day for prayer and rest. Business activities were nil. Occasionally groups of teenagers dressed in Sunday togs would walk down on the wharf and amuse themselves by commenting on the rigging and different characteristics of the schooner's design. In bright gold letters on the black-painted hull planking of the bows was the vessel's name. Highlighted before and after the first and last letters with a vine leaf scroll in gold-leaf paint, and at the stern across the counter taffrail (again in gold-leaf) was the name *Western Belle* and the word "Halifax". Between the two words a symbol in the shape of a compass pointed downward across a ninety degree square, in such a manner that the two instruments framed the letter "G". This symbol, a common sight found on both Nova Scotia and New England schooners, was displayed in the same manner on the name board at the stern. The arrangement served to provide passing ships with the schooner's name, the home port of registry and a fraternal greeting of goodwill and friendship exchanged from ship to ship, through the medium of symbol, as they glided past each other on the high seas. However, the *Western Belle* was all secured in port that day. But the excellent workmanship in the letters, scroll and symbol, which glistened in the sunlight, was an outstanding attraction for young and old who included Whitman's Wharf in their Sunday afternoon walk.

St. Peters Canal and the Bras D'Or Lakes

Chapter 9

Typical of Nova Scotia weather in the month of April, Monday morning dawned with the sun rising up through a bank of heavy cloud. Described by many a mariner as a "high dawn" along this coast, it indicates a strong wind from a southerly direction (what seafaring people call "a strong breeze"); in velocity, one could be safe in estimating it at twenty to thirty miles per hour. There was one favourable service in this strong southerly (if strong winds do have any favourable service). With the Gulf Stream directly off shore, and flowing northward across the entire southeast coast of Nova Scotia, it would be only a matter of a few hours before the effect of the warm Stream water would be carried shoreward in the atmosphere and would warm up the entire coast. This then would start growth in the fertile sections of coastline, and best of all for the Canso area, would, as these people say, "sink the ice" and clear up that hazard to permit shore fishing to commence.

Soon after daylight, men's voices could be heard up on the wharf where the *Western Belle* lay at Canso. The same was true on the two wharfs at Queensport where the other two schooners were waiting to discharge the cargo of salt and canning material. Both cargoes were essential to the start of the season's activities and arrived at a time when they must be in the correct place and ready for use. However, by noon rain began to fall, and suddenly ended the operation of discharging salt.

Captain Abe made good use of the idle time by going ashore and was fortunate enough to visit another fish firm that gave him a charter to carry a cargo of green salt codfish (salted cod that had not been through the drying process). These had been caught just before the freeze-up in January and were now sold to a firm in Lunenburg. On completion of delivery of that consignment of salt fish, he was to proceed to the barrel factory at Chester Basin to load and deliver in Canso five hundred empty mackerel and herring barrels. This charter he was quite satisfied with, because all crew members, with the exception of Jack, would be at home when at Chester Basin. Jack's home was down the Eastern Shore in the St. Mary's River district.

Up in Queensport, opportunities were equally good for charters. The *Maud G.* was contracted to go to Sydney, Cape Breton, to bring coal for the cannery. Captain Mose Griffin had the choice of going to the Magdalen Islands for a load of fresh herring for fish bait, or load up with green salt fish for Halifax and bring a load of empty barrels back from Chester. The latter he accepted.

The weather conditions Tuesday were better and the business of discharging salt continued. However, it was wet, with a cold easterly wind, and fog. The warm southerly wind, blowing in over the ice and cold water, developed into a large area of fog that blanketed the entire coast. By noon, the last of the cargo of salt was discharged and the schooner immediately moved over to the wharf where the new cargo of salted codfish began coming on board. Long wooden chutes carried the fish from the shed doors right down on board the schooner, where several men were employed piling the fish, back downwards and evenly spread — the manner in which green salted codfish must be packed to prevent breaking and destroying the product.

At Queensport, the *Lucy B.* was also under the chutes and her cargo of salted codfish was being loaded. Captain Hodson had the *Maud G.* underway, and through the blanket of dense fog, was crossing the bay in a northeasterly direction to enter the Lennox Passage. This passage is the narrow seaway between Isle Madame and Cape Breton Island and leads into St. Peters and the canal to the great Bras d'Or Lakes. Small schooners may thus make the passage via inland waters from Chedabucto Bay across and out on the northeast coast of Cape Breton Island into the Cabot Strait. This route made the distance from Queensport to Sydney thirty miles shorter and avoided the hazardous passage of rounding Cape Scatari, which at its best is usually a choppy piece of water to navigate. However, the strong current that can reach three knots' velocity setting in and out of the Gut of Canso every six hours,

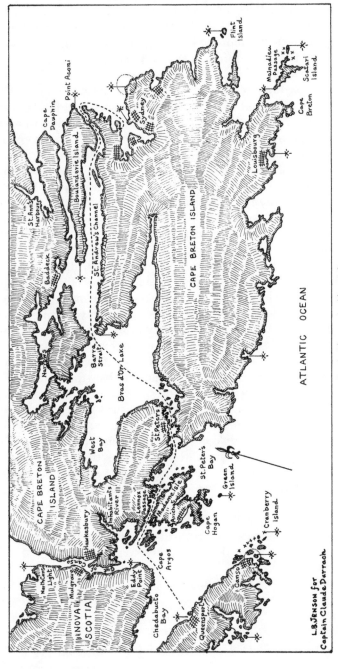

ATLANTIC OCEAN

Route taken by Maud G.

L.B.JENSEN for
Captain Claude Darrach.

caused Captain Bill plenty of concern during that section of the route that lies between Cape Argos and Inhabitants River. At that point, and near the shore of Cape Breton Island, the wind blowing from off the land thinned the fog considerably and Captain Hodson could see approximately one half mile. This made it possible for him to traverse the narrow passage, and arrive at Bourgeois Inlet, and come to anchor in a sheltered locality before dark shut down. Only the short distance of four miles was left to sail next morning to reach the St. Peters Canal locks and enter the Lakes for the passage of approximately fifty miles.

After clearing Cape Argos the course turned more to the north for a distance of approximately three miles until Rabbit Island was sighted, close on the starboard bow. At this point, the course again was altered and the little schooner was heading east through the narrow Lennox Passage, less than one mile wide. Fortunately the ebb tide favoured the schooner and helped increase her speed in the light puffs of wind that varied considerably in direction as they baffled down off the hills on either side. The waterway is so much obstructed at this point that it has been a simple matter to construct a drawbridge for the convenience of land travel from Madame Island to Cape Breton Island proper. Also, it is here that we see a unique drawbridge worked by a horse-operated capstan. On the approach of a vessel, the narrow highway is blocked off by a boom gate, the horse is hitched up to the capstan-bar traces, and walks in a circle to wind the bridge open and provide a gap through which a coastal vessel may pass. As a safety measure, sailing vessels must lower all head-sails, and warp lines are put ashore to prevent the passing vessel from damaging the bridge construction. The toll fee is paid without delay as the craft slowly passes through the gap, and soon after, the warp lines are let go and the vessel is once again on her own, to be skillfully conned closely past Dog Island, and on eastward to Grande Digue Point Lighthouse, into the wider and deeper waters of St. Peters Bay, where sufficient space exists to manoeuver a sailing vessel, regardless of the direction from which the wind blows. Then the long concrete seawalls of the locks are entered.

Again sails are lowered and one passes through the locks in the same manner as in any other seaway where water levels vary from one area to another.

However, as Captain Hodson had reckoned, it was dark when the light breeze had carried them to a position one half-mile south of Quetique Island. The sails were lowered and the anchor dropped for the night. This for Captain Bill was a good day's run; he had reached a good vantage point on the voyage.

Next morning, with the rising sun, came a fresh southeasterly breeze for which Captain Bill was more than thankful. He knew the narrow six-mile passage from the Canal on, in to Gregory Island, which, at points, is less than five hundred feet wide and where hills rise almost straight up to an elevation of two hundred and ninety feet. It's from off these steep cliffs that the violent puffs of wind strike down on a sailing vessel without warning and play the same mean tricks of breaking off masts and destroying sails, as the mythical one-eyed giant Cyclops played on Ulysses on his return home from the Trojan War. Out on the open sea, wind is fairly steady with very little variation in velocity or force. But when navigating through peculiar inland waterways, where high hills rise straight up from the water, atmospheric conditions create violent bursts of revolving squalls that strike without warning and only the strongest rigging can survive. And so, that first six miles of sailing the narrow, picturesque, winding route past steep capes and islands demanded skillful seamanship and a keen lookout.

The *Maud G.* was in the lock basin and her skipper waiting at the control office to request haul to the Bras d'Or Lakes bright and early. The details of ownership, cargo, and displacement of the craft, were recorded, and the machinery put into operation for swinging the large lock-gates open and shut so that the little schooner would be elevated those few feet to the level, and on into the Bras d'Or Lakes.

Having cleared the lock, and on the lake proper, no time was lost in hoisting the sails most suitable for manoeuvering the crooked narrow route out from St. Peters Inlet. Currents at this point are almost non-existent, which reduces considerably the danger of grounding. However, the anchor is always ready for immediate use just in case a freak puff of wind heads the vessel off course toward the shore.

Captain Bill relaxed when he passed clear of Gregory Island and pointed the schooner on a northeasterly course for the fifteen mile run across the lake to enter the Barra Strait; into the waters of Grand Narrows, another picturesque trip, of approximately thirty miles, in an easterly heading that leads out to Point Aconi and the broad Atlantic Ocean; then less than ten miles to the coal pier at Sydney Harbor.

This is the one place, that in less time than it takes to change your mind, you find the clean white canvas sails, the nice white paint, all the neat coils of hemp and manila rope halyards, cargo, and even the whiskers on your face, entirely coated with that fine black coal-dust which just stays with you as long as the cargo is coal. No doubt, like all other ship owners, Captain Bill was consoling himself with the thought that being able to have a cargo loaded on in less than two hours, and turned toward the port of consignment, meant money, and money earned from a coal cargo was clean money. And the ocean supplied plenty of free water with which to wash down once the cargo had been discharged. Captain Bill and his crew were battling the coal-dust while enjoying smooth sailing through sheltered inland waterways.

It was a far different story out on the southeast coast of Nova Scotia, where both the *Lucy B.* and *Western Belle* were en route from Canso to Halifax and Lunenburg in one of the thickest fog-banks of the season. There was a fresh southwest wind and dense fog — that dreaded cold, wet atmospheric condition which reduces visibility to practically nil, and creates distinct drops of condensation on every strand of rope and every thread of canvas — even your eyebrows and whiskers become coated with that clear, cold water. It chills you to the bone and you just shiver while looking and listening for other ships that might be closing up on your course.

The two schooners, unaware of each other's location, were less than ten miles apart. The distance over a straight course from Canso to Halifax is close to one hundred and thirty miles; from Canso to Lunenburg, more like one hundred and sixty miles. But now under sail and with southwest winds, the course would definitely not be straight. Tacking to windward would increase the distance by at least twenty per cent.

The art of coastal navigation, good judgment, ability to use a chart, parallel rulers and compass, are the qualifications a master is required to have, if he is to be confident of and responsible for making safe passage under such conditions. Both Captain Abe and

90

Captain Mose had all this, along with years of experience, and they were not the type to lose valuable time in port waiting for fine, clear weather.

Like Abe, so did Captain Mose take time to plot the assumed courses on the charts before leaving port, and in doing so both were grateful to the Government's Department of Marine and Fisheries for the establishment of fog-horn sound signals located at various points along the coast.

Cranberry Island at the south entrance of Canso Harbour was the last land sighted by the *Western Belle* as she passed within one hundred yards of the lighthouse. The wind was from the southwest and the schooner headed off on a course of one hundred and seventy degrees magnetic. Captain Abe allowed 5° for leeway and plotted his courses on a make-good track of 60°, which means that when the sails are trimmed and the vessel tacking into the wind, the relative angle at which she will sail to the direction from which the wind blows, is 60°. In the case of the *Western Belle,* the wind blew from southwest, which is 225°, and when sailing with the sails out on the port-side she points and makes good an angle of 165°, and when sailing with the sails out on the starboard side she would point and make good a relative course of 285°.

The art of plotting a track is to fix the apex of the off-shore angle so that the on-shore tack would lead to the area in which a fog horn could be heard. This would serve to check the vessel's position as she nears the land through the dense fog when the visibility is less than one hundred yards.

Under Four Lowers Chapter 10

As the blurred glimpse of Cranberry Island was lost in the fog bank, Mate Publicover completed the operation of streaming the log and proceeded directly to the cabin, noted the time by the cabin clock, and made an entry in the large black-covered book on the master's desk, an entry that read:

"2.20 p.m. Cran By Isl. — log O. Wind SW. Fog Thick standing off."

After this he returned on deck and informed Captain Abe the log was set twenty after two. Abe, who was standing on the windward quarter watching and conning the vessel off shore and out clear of the surrounding ledges, gave the mate a nod in the affirmative and repeated the time, "Twenty after two".

The log that Bill Publicover had streamed was not like the present day bridge and taffrail reading type. It was a real pioneer in mechanical ships' distance recording mechanisms. The famous old Harpoon Log with a revolving fan tail attached to a built-in recording instrument, it had to be hauled back on board each time it was read. This meant hauling back approximately forty fathoms of line, the distance the log would be towed astern. The actual distance varied with the size and speed of the vessel, but the principal idea was to have the instrument towed as much as possible parallel to the surface, and far enough away from the vessel, to be clear of the wake or broken water of the vessel towing it.

One half-hour later, Captain Abe became more relaxed. He knew now that the Bull and Cape Breakers were a safe distance astern, and that once again he had the *Western Belle* out on the open sea, close hauled under four lowers with a good fifteen knot southwest breeze, and a thick fog that lowered the visibility to less than one hundred yards. He reckoned he had lots of time to go down the forecastle for a mug of tea and one of the cook's ginger buns, and be on deck again at twenty past three to haul the log and determine the rate of speed (per hour) the vessel was doing. Then he would plot her course further up along the coast, in such a manner as to close in on the fog horns at Whitehead and Beaver Island, and make use of their sound signals to check the vessel's position.

At three twenty-five, the skipper had learned from the log that the old schooner was reeling off eight knots an hour. This speed he needed to know with some accuracy in order to plot the track to sail and tack on, to be closest inshore where he could hear, in sufficient time, the vibrating howl, produced by the well-adjusted diaphone on shore. This sound, under normal choppy weather conditions, could be heard three miles away.

Mate Bill Publicover and Reuben Zinck were on watch from two p.m. until four p.m., each steering for one hour and keeping lookout for one hour. At four p.m. they would be relieved by the skipper and Madera for the next two hours, and in this manner would the routine continue until they arrived in port.

Abe's watch below was spent with his prized possession, a new Admiralty survey chart. Using his parallel rulers, he laid off a course 160° magnetic from Cranberry Island, marking it in light pencil on the chart. He had allowed 5° for leeway, since he felt the choppy southwest whitecaps would push the old schooner slightly off course. Focussing his glance on Whitehead Island he noted the abbreviations "GP. Fl. (4) ev. 24 s. Dia. (1) ev. 20 sec." These Abe understood to mean at night a group flashing light making four distinct bright flashes every twenty-four seconds; and during thick snow or foggy weather, by day or night, the diaphone fog-horn sounded one blast every twenty seconds. The geographical location of Whitehead Island is approximately twelve miles west of Cranberry Island and almost parallel with the coast line. However, no sailing craft of that type could sail west with a southwest wind, and thus the reason why *Western Belle* was heading off shore on a course of 160° was in order to come about and head up on the 280° course, and pass a safe two or three miles seaward of Whitehead, where they would hear and get bearings of the horn to check on course and speed.

The next fog-horn on the coast was at Beaver Island; ("Dia. ev. min.") meaning "one blast every minute", two different characteristics especially designed so that a simple identification could be made without difficulty, even when being heard at a long distance or the maximum range of sound for the capacity of the horn.

Fifteen minutes past three o'clock, the skipper returned on deck, and assisted by Mate Publicover, commenced hauling the log line inboard on the after section of the starboard side, and with a running turn around the mooring post, allowed the same line to run over the stern fairlead and out behind the vessel. In this manner, when the instrument was brought out of the water and on board, the entire length of the log line was now trailing astern, with the ends opposite. On bringing the log carefully inboard, Captain Abe pushed open the sliding brass plate that protected the glass-covered clock face and noted the tachometer readings: three little circular dials — the first graduated in tenths of one mile, the second in ten miles, and the third in one hundred miles. The one tenth dial registered two, the ten mile dial registered six and the one hundred mile dial moved away very slightly from zero.

"Six point two, he says," quoted Abe after a careful look at the dials, and without unnecessary delay, closed the protection plate.

As Mate Publicover hauled in the log line, Captain Abe lowered the instrument back in the water over the stern, paying out the entire forty fathoms of line as it was pulled on board by the strong-armed mate. Finally the end appeared and the skipper braced himself, holding on to the line while the mate proceeded to secure the end to a ringbolt, specially located on a bulwark stanchion. Ordinary twisted manila or hemp rope is not suitable for use in this case. A log line is woven or plaited purposely to withstand the twisting influence caused by the fan-tail rotator. Unless it is streamed out immediately on being brought in, it will curl and kink in such a manner that it would be impossible to untangle for hours.

"Six knots. Now, when it comes twenty to four o'clock, we will be eight miles off, far enough to come about and head up shore for Whitehead fog-horn."

With this remark, Abe pushed back the companionway slide and descended to his sanctum sanctorum (the cabin) knowing that soon now he would be returning to the deck for a two-hour watch.

He dressed himself in a pair of oilskin trousers, donned a three-quarter length reefer coat and his heavy, navy blue melton cap. He glanced at the little brown jug that was partly hidden in the coils of a pile of ready-to-use manila rope lying on the cabin floor, but remembering he was at sea under conditions that demanded clear thinking and quick action, the little brown jug was not disturbed from its lashings. He sat on the cabin locker and, with long experience and skill in filling a pipe to suit the occasion, cut off small chunks of tobacco and dropped them in the old, seasoned pipe bowl, one by one, until she was loaded to the gunwales, pressed the filling gently with his thumb and tried her out for draught. Abe knew enough about pipe smoking not to fill up with fine-cut and go on the deck of a schooner under sail with lee scuppers awash.

The brass minute hand of the cabin clock was crawling up on the figure eight as Abe finished the second and successful attempt to get the pipe lighted. At this he ascended to the deck and shouted the order:

"Ready for stays."

This, in windjammer language, tells the foreward look-out to stand by the jib sheets and be ready for tacking ship, and, by the same token, causes the helmsman to give the sails a good fill of wind so that the vessel picks up to a maximum speed and momentum. When the wind spills out of the sails as she points into the wind's eye while coming about, there is sufficient momentum to keep moving ahead until all sails have crossed over and sheets are trimmed on the opposite tack.

"Hard alee!" is the next order.

At this the helmsman spins the wheel over in the direction in which the vessel's bow is to be turned. At that moment there begins a tremendous roar and rattle of canvas, ropes and blocks with approximately four thousand square feet of heavy, damp canvas slatting in the wind. It only lasts for seconds while the vessel changes course from 165° over an arc of 120° and is steadied on course 285°, the relative angle of a SW wind that an average fore-and-aft rigged schooner will sail, close hauled.

At this point, Skipper Abe relieved the helmsman and began his one hour trick of steering, while his watch-mate, Madera, kept lookout from a forward section of the vessel. Madera's position for that hour was not an enviable one, by any means. It was his job to sight in sufficient time any on-coming object, and act as required to direct the man at the wheel how to alter course and avoid colliding or grounding, depending on whatever situation might arise. With the visibility reduced to one hundred yards, and cold wet spray flying back in one's face quite frequently, well, it can only be rated as a rugged job and a responsible one.

Western Belle, however, was now heading toward her destination on the long leg of her windward tacking of the westward passage.

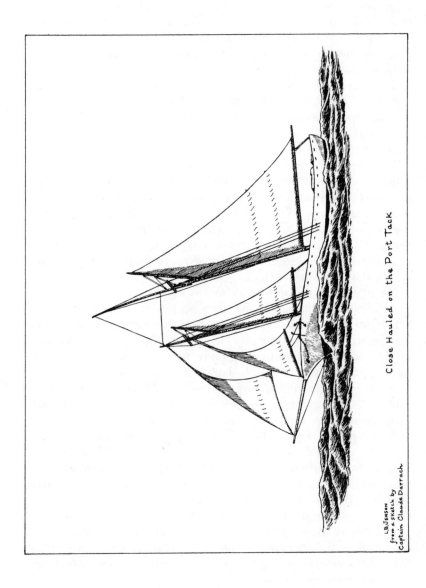

Close Hauled on the Port Tack

L.B.Jensen
from a sketch by
Captain Claude Darrach

The plotting on the chart gave a distance of almost fifteen miles to sail on the port tack before Whitehead fog alarm would be abeam (right angles to the course 285°). So there would be two hours of clear, open-water sailing before the approach to shore and existing danger.

Closing in on other vessels unseen in the fog was always the dread, and "Alert!" was the constant routine of the watch on deck. Abe occasionally took his gaze off the compass and sails to stare into the fog-bank, and he pondered over that admirable verse of Psalm 107: *"They that go down to the sea in ships and occupy their business in great waters. These men see the works of the Lord; and His wonders in the deep."* Like so many more men of the same calling Skipper Abe marvelled at the wisdom in the words of this Psalm.

At times *Western Belle* was heeled over with her dead-eyes awash and her rigging and halyards straining and groaning with every heave and lurch the vessel made. The smoke from the forecastle stove pipe assured the deck watch that good old Jack was on the job and that if nothing else, they would be rewarded with a warm, wholesome supper when coming off duty. During a passage of this sort, only the watch would be seen on deck; working on a basis of twelve hours out of twenty-four, it was necessary to take advantage of every minute below and rest, so as to be wide awake and fit when time came round to be on deck duty.

From where the man stood at the wheel steering, he could also hear the bells of the cabin clock as they struck off the one-half and full hours. By this he could reckon approximately the distance the vessel had traversed and also the time of calling out the next watch, or the time of hauling the log to check distance.

Skipper Abe had completed his trick at the wheel and for some time now was forward in the bow on lookout duty. Millwood Jack, who had spent most of the day below in the forecastle cooking and baking, had perched himself almost at the top of the forecastle companionway ladder, with his face above deck in the shelter of the open scuttle, enjoying a breath of fresh air. It was twenty to six now and Publicover and Zinck were eating supper prior to coming on watch. Jack pricked up his ears and stood motionless so as to hear again and confirm his imagination that he actually had heard the dull low groan of a fog-horn. Sure enough, again the sound came, and again. By this time he had become brave enough to make the announcement to the skipper, which he did, but in a non-committal manner.

"You hear that horn, Skipper?" shouted Jack from his companionway perch.

"Not yet, Cook."

"Then I do, from the scuttle here, pretty far. But it's him all right, Skipper. I count twenty-eight, old man, and he boo again every time."

"You count him slow next time, Cook! Count him one and two, and three, and four, next time, Cook!"

For a while there was nothing said, then finally Jack announced:

"He be twenty and *boo* and twenty and *boo*, Skipper."

"Well, I guess that's him, Cook, but the bow wave and noise on deck drowns him out from here, so far."

But by now Abe's ears were picking up the *boo-oo's* and he commenced the business of checking the direction from which the sound was coming so as to plot an estimated position on the chart. Mate Bill Publicover was on deck now, ready to take over the watch, and both he and the skipper agreed on the bearing and range of the horn. Publicover's presence on deck gave Abe the opportunity to go to the cabin and work on the chart. By six o'clock it was agreed that the horn was abeam (90° to the course) and at least three miles away. The log was hauled and it read an even twenty-four miles. At this time Abe made another entry in the black covered book: "6 p.m. Whitehead — 3¹/₃ log 24 wind S.W. and thick fog."

A study of the chart showed that they could continue on the same course for another nine or ten miles and be out of danger from reefs or shoals, and Abe decided on doing that rather than standing off-shore again. He was also pleased to note that on this port tack and heading westward, they had increased speed up to seven and one quarter knots.

Six p.m. was past now and Publicover and Zinck were on deck with the watch turn. Skipper Abe, having been quite content with the service the fog alarm had provided, went below and joined his watch mate, Madera, and Cook Jack to enjoy a hot supper of fresh hot buns and schooner hash. Don't for one minute underestimate that menu! The best quality western corn beef, turnips, potatoes and onions properly cooked and made into schooner hash will satisfy the appetite of any man and provide the hardiness required to face the elements of the sea.

Abe was below deck taking the weight off his feet, but not relaxed or resting particularly now, while carrying on sail and driving a schooner through thick fog and choppy sea. By seven thirty he calculated the position to be approximately three miles ESE of Brandy Ledges, and gave the order to tack ship and stand offshore for the night. On second thought, he hauled the log and got a reading of thirty-three point seven miles. This checked with his dead reckoning, but he was sure that there could well be a correction of one or two miles to account for, and tacking off shore was the proper way to take care of that correction.

Sighted in the Nick of Time   Chapter 11

Abe's thoughts often drifted back to his rival friend, Mose, and the schooner *Lucy B*. He knew she, too, was close hauled under four lowers not far away, and also that her trim lines would log off a faster speed than the cumbersome *Western Belle*. Both schooners were well ballasted with roughly one hundred and eighty thousand pounds of salt codfish, deep in the water and ploughing along through the choppy sou'wester with lee decks awash most of the time.

The *Lucy B*. passed about ten miles off Cape Canso shortly before six o'clock. She had stood well off shore before coming on the port tack to head westerly, while punching her way along at a good eight knots. The keen eye of lookout Duggan Tanner sighted a dory sail close off the port bow. This, he knew, meant only one thing which called for immediate action. It was a lost fishing dory from a banking schooner that must be rescued before night. Tanner ran aft toward where Asa Gook, the mate, was steering, pointing and shouting at the top of his voice.

"A dory! A lost dory!"

The mate, without hesitation, brought the schooner head into the wind, spilled the wind out of the sails and slowed her speed down to almost a slow jog. However, by this time the dory and schooner had lost sight of each other in the fog and were at least one half mile apart.

All this commotion brought Captain Mose and the others on deck in short notice; the sudden unscheduled thundering of canvas slatting and the vessel's trembling brings all hands on deck. Skipper Mose did not see the dory, but his judgment gave him a good idea of where and how to find it. He ordered the cook to get the hand horn and keep it sounding constantly, and ordered the others to stand by to tack ship.

Lucy's ability to manoeuver well saved precious minutes now and she was soon over on the starboard tack, heading back on her own track.

100

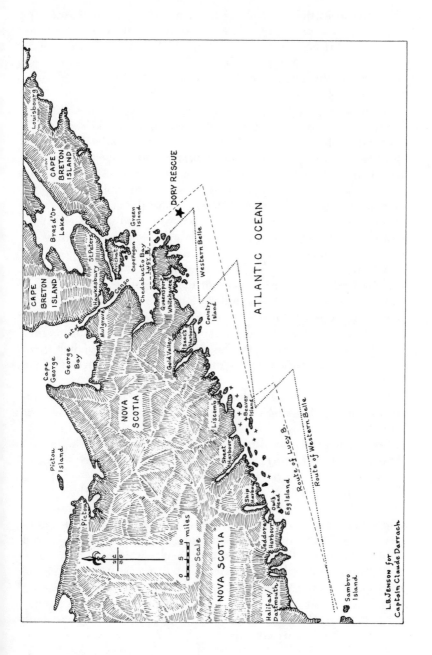

DORY RESCUE

Louisbourg

CAPE BRETON ISLAND

Brasd'Or Lake

CAPE BRETON ISLAND

St Peters

Hawkesbury

Mulgrave

Guts

Canso

Green Island

Capehegan

Chedabucto Bay

Lucy Bay

Queensport

Whitehaven

Western Belle

Cape George

George Bay

NOVA SCOTIA

Gold Valley

Isaacs Harbour

Country Island

Pictou Island

Pictou

Liscomb

Beaver Island

Sheet Harbour

ATLANTIC OCEAN

Ship Harbour

Owl's Head

Egg Island

Route of Lucy B.

Route of Western Belle

Jeddore

Harbour

Halifax/Dartmouth

NOVA SCOTIA

Sambro Island

Scale

0   5   10 miles

L.B.JENSON for
Captain Claude Darrach.

"Lower away the outer jib," was the next order, and Mose let go the wheel long enough to slack off the main sheet, and kept the vessel well off before the wind. With the big mainsail now full of free wind, *Lucy* began to step up to a good ten knots. Only a few minutes and the men in the bow shouted:

"There it is, just off to port and two men are in it!"

Again it was only minutes and they were out of sight and separated in the fog; but this time each understood the other's manoeuver. It was now for Mose to get to the lee of the dory, heave the schooner to, keep the fog horn blasting, and hope the dorymen had sufficient strength to bring the dory alongside. About five long minutes later, sure enough, the dory was again sighted riding the crest of the waves and heading down toward the *Lucy*. The sail was clewed up and both men were using oars and appeared to be strong enough to cope with the job of getting alongside safely. As the newly painted yellow dory closed in on the *Lucy*, it was pitching and heaving at an angle clearly showing that it contained several hundred pounds of fresh cod and haddock. The number "four" was painted on both bows. Finally it was brought alongside; the bowsman flipped in his oars, as only a fisherman can do, and in an instant was throwing the dory's painter (a rope approximately fifty feet long) to the men on the *Lucy's* deck, who pulled them alongside, helped them safely out of the dory and on board the schooner.

Captain Mose left his station at the wheel and joined the men on the quarter-deck asking how long they had been lost and how they were feeling.

"We feels pretty good now, sir, to be on board a vessel again. This would be the third night for us without anything to eat 'cept a few fish hearts we ate a couple hours ago."

While the *Lucy's* crew were engaged in throwing the fish on board and hoisting the dory, Mose took the two men to his cabin and treated each to a small portion of Demerara rum. They both were weak and trembling, much more so than they had realized while in the dory. They had last seen their own schooner, the large Nova Scotia salt banker *Aramada*, two days before when fishing on the south peak thirty miles SSE of Sable Island. They were heading in for the Nova Scotia coast, but had little idea of where they actually were. Crossman and Tanner were their names and both were from Lunenburg county.

"Nothing more to drink now, boys, until you get something to eat and an hour or two in a warm bunk. So be on your way to the forecastle now and the cook will see that you get taken care of."

Mose followed them on deck and, when he saw them go down the forecastle and also saw the dory secured on deck, he ordered the jib hoisted and asked for a hand to trim the main sheet. Dark was closing down now as Mose saw the sheets trimmed to his satisfaction and filled the *Lucy* away with all four lowers full and the lee rail awash. Musson claimed the trick at the wheel now and took over from the skipper who proceeded to the forecastle to be sure the two survivors were given a small light meal, and not one of Munro's "seaman's specials." It was not the place to get a serious stomach disorder, and the wrong food, or too much, all of a sudden to a hungry, weak man could cause trouble. The cook knew he must heed the captain's orders, and the two survivors were on a diet for the next twenty-four hours. Three hours later, Mose ordered the vessel hove to for a depth sounding.

"Twenty-six fathoms to the rail," was the announcement from Mate Gook as he felt the fourteen pound lead strike the ocean floor and sighted the marking near his hand.

Mose filled the *Lucy* away for a few minutes and then ordered, "Hard alee!" to put her on the starboard tack and head off shore. He was not using a log and had kept off shore too far to hear Whitehead fog-horn as they passed by. Mose was calculating his position to be six miles SE from Country Island, and, like Captain Abe, was planning his track to lead up off Beaver Island during the daylight hours next day.

"Lucy B." takes the Lead   Chapter 12

Darkness had settled down now and the heavy, low, wet fog reduced the visibility to fifty yards and less, and the wind was gusty. Both skippers carried on all four lowers during the night, and arranged that both deck watch men stay close together and near the wheel for the dark hours. Clear green water came in over the bow and along back aft on quite frequent occasions, as the schooners plunged into the southwest swells that rolled down with the wind. Heading off on the starboard tack and bucking into the choppy sea reduced the speed to six knots. Although unseen by each other, the *Lucy B.* and *Western Belle* were much closer together than their skippers realized. *Lucy B.*, by far the best sailor under these conditions, had crept up and closed the gap between the two.

When the watch changed at two a.m., both vessels had come about on the port tack and were heading up shore toward Beaver Island. They also found that the wind had veered and was blowing from the south, which allowed the vessels to alter course and steer up for Sambro Island, a more direct course toward their destination. Sailing with eased sheets, and the southwest swell hitting them on the quarter rather than on the bows, made life much more comfortable. The south wind brought rain. Soon the fog lifted and, by five a.m. and daylight, the three schooners were in sight of each other with a hazy visibility of less than three miles. Abe recognized the nearest vessel to him to be a Gloucester halibut fisherman. She was heading southeastward and was a picture: two large stacks of yellow-painted dories on her deck, and a large suit of sails that were cut and sewn to perfection. She would be roughly four hundred miles from her home port now, and would have at least two hundred more to reach the Stone Fence (the well-known halibut fishing ground of the Banquereau Bank) and Gully Halibut Banks. In order to be capable of racing home to market (a distance of six hundred miles) with a cargo of fresh, iced halibut, the vessel had to be able and fast. Shortening sail was seldom if ever practised aboard a fresh fisherman bound for market unless some weak strands gave way and the sail blew out of the bolt ropes.

The trim, long, black sides, lofty masts and enormous spread of sail was a beautiful sight in the eyes of the windjammer seamen. The other sail, barely visible in the hazy cloud, looked the same to Captain Abe as it did to the captain of the other schooner, who happened to be none other than Captain Mose Griffin and the *Lucy B.*

With daylight, the wind became moderate and rain showers fell in cloudbursts. The atmosphere would suddenly change temperature: sometimes a pocket of very warm air, then in an instant, a cool, piercing, light air would replace the warm. Abe had been paying special attention to this phenomenon and knew it was a warning of a change of wind and probably plenty of it. The sea also was rough now, and confused swells were rolling in opposite directions, meeting and piling up in odd-shaped pyramids until they would lose momentum and support, then fall over back on the surface with a *slop, smack,* sound. This made a continuous loud splashing, gurgling noise until sufficient wind came and changed the whole surface.

Abe called all hands and ordered a reef put in the mainsail. This procedure called for lowering the big sail and shortening the luff and leach with the help of jack rope and reef pennants. The lower section of the sail was folded neatly and tied by reef points between boom and bolt rope. The sail, thus reduced by about twenty percent, was then hoisted again and being less lofty, enabled the vessel to carry on without overtaxing spars and rigging.

The first procedure, out in an open, confused sea, calls for seamanship and skill. A wood crutch is erected, the boom is lowered and slipped into the jaws of the crutch, which is located at the extreme stern end of the vessel. On the instant the boom comes to rest in the crutch, port and starboard tackles have to be attached to the boom and secured down to ringbolts in the bulwark stanchion set up bar tight and belayed to prevent the long boom from swaying while the reef is being tied in. This gives the man who has to go out on the end of the boom a chance to work with some sense of security.

The operation of reefing the mainsail used up almost half an hour and occupied everyone's thoughts as well as time. When the sail was reset and sheeted again, the crew had a chance to size up matters. The visibility had continued to improve sufficiently now so that the vessels were recognizable to each other. Abe had no alternative but to admit the *Lucy B.* was a smart little vessel under sail, but consoled himself with the thought that the *Western Belle* had the heaviest and best paying cargo to drag along.

Northerly Squalls Chapter 13

Finally both schooners encountered the same conditions, all within minutes of each other. The head sails fell inboard, gave a few slaps port and starboard, and, without further warning but with grace and effort, main and foresails also came inboard and across decks to favor the port side. All hands automatically became engaged in trimming sheets and altering course to keep the sails filled with wind. The sky broke through the wet hazy atmosphere, and heavy cumulo-stratus cloud coming out from the north signalled the front of the on-coming wind with which they would soon have to contend. It was moving toward them quite quickly and the water became a series of southerly lops, cocking up and facing a strong current of northerly atmosphere that pushed against them *smack, splash,* and influenced them to head back south. The wind, for the past hour, had been less than one knot velocity, but now fresh puffs were filling the sails and supplying enough resistance to stop the schooners from rolling with the swell as they had been free to do during the calm. By nine a.m. the cumulo-stratus front had passed over and brought an increasing north wind, the sky was filled with cumulo-cirrus cloud and the sea was a series of white caps and blue wind squalls.

Both schooners were again on the starboard tack heading WNW and lee rails awash. Mose, gambling on the fact that he had sufficient men on board to lower and reef the mainsail during heavy weather, had not yet reefed, and this had old Abe very much concerned. Deep down, his thoughts were causing him to debate with himself whether or not he had practiced good seamanship and done the right thing, or if he was getting a wee bit too careful. This bothered him, in spite of the fact that the old schooner at times had lots of green water along her lee quarter-deck, and he was sure that the *Lucy* was washing the lee side of her cabin house. On board the *Lucy,* Captain Mose was now kicking himself for not reefing when he could have done so without any doubt of getting the sail hoisted up again. *Lucy* was washing, and much, too much, to be properly

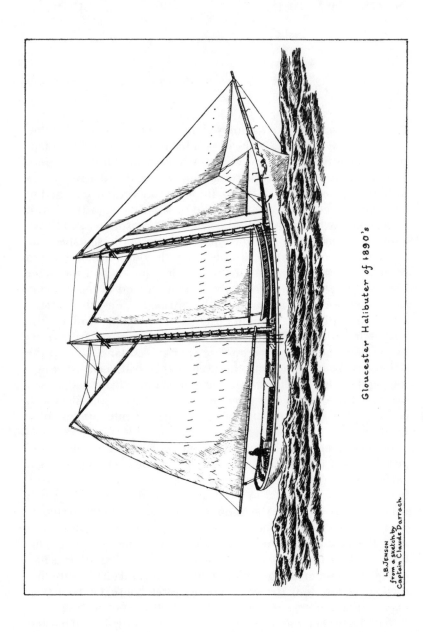

Gloucester Halibuter of 1890's

L.B.Jenson.
from a sketch by
Captain Claude Darrach.

sailed. More evidence of his mistake was the fact that *Western Belle* was footing faster and going away from the *Lucy*. Abe was not slow to note this very satisfactory state of affairs that favored his position, and was more pleased half an hour later when he saw that rival Mose was manoeuvering to reef down.

Mose had left it too late, and was now faced with a much more difficult job. He would also have to lower the outer jib, a small sail of lighter canvas, that cannot stand too much slapping or abuse, and called for secure lashings when lowered. It's not really safe to go out on a bowsprit to furl a jib with a schooner heading into the wind and choppy sea. Nor is it easy or safe to swing off and run before the wind with a full mainsail set, in heavy wind.

Mose was biting hard on a chew of tobacco and trying to figure out the best move. Finally he eased the vessel up close into the wind and ordered the jib lowered. As the halyards were eased away, the sail fell to the bowsprit and hung down, slapping and dragging, in the water — a dangerous situation for an outer jib. Then he ordered the mainsail eased down. There was too much wind and chop to get the crutch erected, but the wind kept the sail fairly steady. Tackles were secured to the boom and the sheet hauled flat and secured. The big sail then was lowered almost all the way down, with the peak kept raised to an angle of about thirty degrees, and left free to swing in the wind. Half of the sail lay over the side and under water, which served a good purpose in that it did not slap or move violently about.

The jib was Mose's greatest concern now. It would be both disasterous and expensive to get it torn to ribbons, and one bad slap, or too much weight of water, could cause that to happen in an instant. Mose put a becket (rope lashing) on the steering wheel and started toward the bow. One of the rescued dorymen, an outstanding sailor, was watching and knew the meaning of the move.

"I'm going with you, old man. We can get him stopped up in some manner. It'd be a shame to get him torn."

From where Mate Gook was perched on the foot ropes of the main boom, he could get the odd sight of the two men working on the bowsprit and getting lashings on the jib. The *Lucy* was more or less hove to now; only the foresail and jumbo were partly filled and she lay wallowing in a choppy sea.

When Mose and the doryman got inboard off the bowsprit, the jib was well secured. It's the skipper's privilege on any vessel to give

109

orders and avoid dangerous chances. But not so with most of these men; they accepted and faced danger when it arose, and will always be respected for doing so. Getting back on the main deck, they joined the job of tying in the reef. By this time half the sail had sunk down under water close along the lee quarter, and was too heavy to be hoisted up. Mose knew the answer to that. He took the becket off the wheel, and swung the vessel off before the wind until she picked up a speed of approximately seven knots. With that momentum, he spun the wheel hard down and as she pointed up into the wind, the sail was towed out on top of the water. As all hands proceeded to pull, it was gradually blown clear of the water and free to come on deck. White sheets of water flew away as the wet canvas slapped and slatted in the wind while the sail was being hoisted. The jib was left on the bowsprit and now *Lucy* was on her way again under reefed mainsail, full foresail and jumbo.

While out to leeward, and ahead, was the now more contented Abe, carrying on all four lowers that included the reefed mainsail. He knew now that he had used the best judgment and was sure Mose would like to have the jib hoisted, if only it were safe to chance getting it up all in one piece. Abe gloried in the arrangement because *Western Belle* could keep up with the *Lucy B.* with the extra sail in use.

Shortly after the heavy wind struck, and knowing that fog does not exist with northerly winds off the Nova Scotia coast, Skipper Abe felt there was no more necessity of towing the log. It was hauled and kept on board. It had registered, in all, fifty-six miles, and when that was applied to the estimated track, it made a dead reckoning position somewhere in the vicinity of fourteen miles SSE from Liscomb Island. By noon all the haze had cleared from the atmosphere and land could be sighted ahead. By one p.m. both schooners were within two miles of each other and approximately five miles off the White Islands. At this point they could alter course from WNW to W, ease off sheets, and achieve about all the speed these schooners can average.

The *Lucy B.* hoisted her jib and picked up considerably more speed. Close under the land where the sea was much less choppy than earlier, when they were further offshore, the two vessels were logging off more than eight knots. Seventy miles to go for Sambro Island and another thirty miles to Lunenburg. With every reason to expect the wind to continue, *Lucy B.* would arrive in Halifax before midnight, and daylight would find *Western Belle* entering Lunenburg Harbour.

The two survivors on board *Lucy* were anxious to get to land and inform their families that they were safe. It would be the practice of the schooner from which the men were lost to return to port and report the men missing, and it was that grim news they hoped to prevent.

When the coastal lighthouses lit their lamps at sundown that evening, *Lucy B.* was passing inward past the twin lights of Devil's Island and entering Halifax Harbour, and *Western Belle* was abeam of Sambro Island, heading up for Cross Island at the entrance to Lunenburg.

Glad Tidings

Chapter 14

Entering Halifax Harbour under sail with a north wind makes for slow progress with a dead beat to windward and several shoals to navigate around, over the eight mile route from Devil's Island to the Halifax waterfront. However, at ten p.m. the *Lucy* had all sails furled and was snugly moored in an inner berth at the Plant Line Steamship pier, and Captain Mose Griffin and the two survivors from the Lunenburg fishing schooner were on their way up town. Telephone was the means of communication required to get the good news home, but none of the three, the skipper nor the two fishermen, was acquainted with the procedure well enough to undertake a long distance call without assistance.

Captain Mose remembered his experience with city policemen and seeing them operate telephones the night he got involved at the "Bucket of Blood" Tavern. He decided the Police Station was the place to go for the necessary assistance, particulary at that time of day. His judgment was good. The desk sergeant immediately called a news reporter from the weekly *Acadian Recorder* newspaper office, who was glad to stand the expense of notifying a clergyman in Lunenburg, reporting the men's names, and that they were well and safe. He relayed to them the word that they could receive instructions the next day via the office of the firm of Boake and Bennet. The reporter, in addition to paying the phone charges, gave each of the survivors a nice token fee for the story of the experience. This time Skipper Mose enjoyed very much having had the police to call on, and agreed they were surely gentlemen when met under the proper circumstances, but doubted if that were possible when meandering ashore with his rival friend Abe!

Three a.m. the next morning a tired and sleepy crew brought the *Western Belle* alongside Lunenburg Outfitters Wharf and got sufficient mooring lines ashore to secure the schooner, and gave the sails a flimsy furl. On the request of the skipper, they brought their mugs to the cabin, and for the first time since casting off at

112

Canso, Abe pulled the cork from the little rum jug, passed the jug to the mate, and gave instructions to make the rounds and fill up the mugs.

"In a time like this, I ain't in the habit of saying 'no'", muttered Zinck, and took good care that the mug got its full share.

Faithful old Jack had both the forecastle stove and the cabin stove well supplied with fuel and a wee spot of red hot iron showing on the cheeks of the bogey. It was "down the hatch and into the bunks" for all hands. They had had a rough passage and were ready for much-needed sleep.

It was nine a.m. next day when Captain Abe climbed ashore to commence attending to business. It was not long before he was told about the *Lucy B.* arriving at Halifax with the two survivors. The news struck Captain Abe in an odd manner, sending his thoughts backward twenty-four hours, and his first remark was:

"Now I understand!" and repeated again, "Now I understand!"

What he actually meant was that he had been very much confused about Mose's move not to reef sail while the wind was moderate and between changes yesterday morning, as he himself had done, but now Abe realized that with the additional help on board, Mose could well gamble on an attempt to carry on all sail in the north wind. And, on the other hand, if during the blow it was necessary to reef, with the extra help it could be done.

"That's why it was Mose kept the full mainsail on so long and was able to get it down, reefed, and up again in the heavy wind," Abe decided.

The procedure for the next two days of unloading the cargo was just normal routine. The fish were hoisted from the vessel, loaded on carts and pulled away by oxen to be washed and spread in the sun on the drying flakes and prepared for the British West India market.

This all worked well and discharging was completed in sufficient time to sail from Lunenburg Harbour to Chester Basin (a short voyage of eighteen miles). This was possibly the nearest port where the *Western Belle* could come to anchor and the captain and most of the crew members would be just about at home. Not more than five miles from the schooner's berth, and all except the cook would be back home after approximately seven weeks' operations along the coast. So, with all the home chores that are required, particularly in spring, Captain Abe declared a week's holiday for all. This of course, was of no advantage to Millwood Jack, the cook, whose home was more than one hundred and fifty miles away and where scheduled transporation just did not exist.

Captain Abe arranged the compensation for that inconvenience by dickering with the manager of the barrel factory to include Jack with the hired people that were contracted to load the empty barrel cargo on board, while the vessel lay in port. In addition to his wages, Abe also paid him one dollar each night for watchman duties, and with such a reward Jack was well pleased and knew his chance would come too and he soon could spend a week ashore.

Lunenburg County is, without a doubt, rated as outstanding among Nova Scotia's municipalities. This is simply because of the many sheltered navigable inlets, its fertile soil, and above all, its thrifty, industrious and God-fearing people. The fraternal and cooperative methods practiced by these people in their everyday life have created a prosperous county. The homesteads are so arranged as to include sufficient land to farm a goodly supply of vegetables, with grain and hay to feed and maintain oxen and beef cattle. Woodlots were capable of producing all the necessary ship building and construction lumber.

So, Captain Abe Young and the crewmen of the *Western Belle* were to be briefly at home on a homestead lot, as already described, where they were anxious to see and assist the other members of the various families that keep the home and farms operating while the men are at sea.

It being noon Saturday when the schooner arrived in her home port and tied up at the narrow head of the small Government Wharf, loading of the new cargo would begin early on Monday morning. Then the shipment of empty barrels would be hauled by teams of local oxen. There was an unwritten law against the practice of working on Sunday in this county, which was highly respected. Sunday togs and church services were the order of the day.

114

A Full Cargo and Flying Light   Chapter 15

Empty barrels are light in weight but bulky in size. This way they fill up the cargo hold and cause the schooner to displace very little more water than when in ballast. Cargo vessels use all hold space for cargo, and room for permanent ballast is sacrificed to it. So, when *Western Belle* had had three hundred and forty empty fish barrels stowed below decks, she was still flying light (a nautical term for a ship floating high in the water) and in no condition to carry sail or endure heavy weather at sea. This is what Captain Abe found Wednesday evening when he made his first visit to the schooner since arriving in port. He had been busy at other work of a different sort, and having been informed by the manager of the barrel factory that the shipment was delivered, he decided to make a call on board to check the situation.

Lobster fishermen, returning from attending lobster pots out in the bay, reported a vessel heading in toward the Basin. Abe imagined this would be the *Lucy B*. and his famous rival friend, Mose Griffin, who, he learned when he was at Canso, would also be carrying empty barrels back to Queensport.

When you arrive at the approaches of Mahone Bay, and commence to enter any of the many sheltered inlets, you are faced with the problem of navigating your craft through a series of islands and shoals. There are at least fifty islands of various sizes in this bay, including Oak Island where it is believed that a pirate treasure, possibly that of Captain Kidd, is buried. (Not much is known of the results, but several thousands of dollars have been paid out to local residents for services rendered with different treasure hunting parties, some of which have included oil drilling experts using special type drills. I've been shipmates with men who were employed on Oak Island expeditions. They all have the greatest respect for the people who hired them and never can be dragged into a detailed discussion of events. I've heard it admitted that old hewn timbers were found deep in the excavations — wood of a sort that does not grow in this country).

"Containers" of an earlier age ready on a wharf,
— a typical cargo for a Schooner —

L.B.JENSON for
Captain Claude Darrach

From what information Captain Abe had received from the lobster fishermen, the schooner *Lucy B.* would be sailing in past Oak Island, just three miles away, at that very moment. The moderate SW wind would be moving the *Lucy* along at an estimated four miles an hour. Abe became aware of the fact that he should man a small rowboat and go out on the bay, meet the schooner, and assist Mose in piloting in to the wharf. This he proceeded to do without delay. When he did get outside the headland of the inlet and was able to get a clear view out to seaward, sure enough, there was the *Lucy B.* traversing the correct channel leading into Chester Basin.

"Good for Mose," pondered Abe, "This is his first time sailing to this port, and he steers a good course."

Abe laid on his oars and waited for the long, black hull of the schooner to come close so that he could pass up a piece of rope to Mate Gook, who was standing in the fore chains. As the small rowboat was dragged alongside, Abe reached up for the lee rigging and pulled himself on board. At first glance he was to find Mose striding up alongside to greet him, and at the same instant, saw that a fisherman from Great Tancook Island was at the wheel conning the vessel up channel.

Mose's first comment was to tell Abe he was too late to collect pilotage fees, and informed him that he had hove the vessel to for awhile off Tancook Island to wait until a fisherman came off and accepted the pilot job.

"Was very glad to have him too, when I saw all the islands sticking out around the bay," he admitted.

It was time now to start lowering the sails and Abe assisted in this manoeuver, being sure that he got up on the cabin house while furling the mainsail. From this vantage point, he could size up the vessel's position and satisfy himself all was well. It's a peculiar sensation for a master to find himself onboard another vessel at sea, having to accept the status of a passenger and hold himself back from giving orders, and also, at the same time, control his anxious nerves while waiting to hear the order for some operation that maybe he, himself, would have had made a minute or so earlier.

Both vessels were berthed at the same wharf. *Western Belle*, having her cargo on board, was held off and *Lucy B.* secured inside on the jetty-head for convenience in loading.

Captain Mose accepted an invitation to visit Captain Abe's home, where he remained until the next morning, and was permitted to return to his schooner with the agreement that he would accept the offer of a room and meals at Abe's home during the remainder of his stay in port.

The *Lucy B.* was sporting a new coat of copper paint on her bottom. She had been hauled out on the Dartmouth Marine Slips, for cleaning off marine growth, and inspection for defects, with particular attention being given to rudder gudgeons and pintles. New bolts had been placed in the bob stay; fastenings at the stern post were drawn and replaced, and seams near the waterline recaulked where the winter ice had damaged and torn out the oakum.

Saturday morning Abe got himself and one other member of his immediate family employed at loading some fifty bushels of potatoes: surplus stock from their cellar bins left over from the winter supply. These would make quick sale down along the Eastern Shore where not enough soil was available to provide homegrown supplies of mixed vegetables. About three thousand feet of good pine boat lumber from the Young chopping was brought from a nearby mill and loaded on deck. This would find a ready market at Port Bickerton or Canso where boat building and repair shops were located.

Captain Mose sailed early Saturday. When the last load of barrels had been delivered, the smaller *Lucy* had two hundred and ninety below deck and seventy-five were secured on the foreward deck. She was calling at Halifax to pick up barreled kerosene oil for Isaac's Harbour and Queensport merchants.

Abe had stocked up with ship's stores while at Lunenburg, and intended sailing Monday with the morning breeze, direct to Canso, if weather permitted. Should a strong blow and choppy sea develop, both vessels would be obliged to make for shelter and wait for reasonably moderate winds and smooth sea. It would be dangerous to risk manoeuvering a light draft schooner so close along the coast in bad weather.

North Bound through the Canso Straits

Chapter 16

The voyage from Chester Basin to Canso and Queensport was a normal voyage, with moderate off-shore winds and good visibility. Each vessel made the trip in less than twenty-four hours' sailing. While the empty barrels were being discharged, news reached the south coast that Northumberland Strait lobster factories were paying sky-high prices for fresh herring from the Magdalen Islands.

The *Maud G.* had discharged the load of coal at Queensport and cleared for Grindstone Island in the Magdalen group. Chartered to deliver a load of fresh caught herring to a lobster factory at Caribou in the Northumberland Strait, by this time she should have arrived and been in the process of taking on the cargo.

Captain Abe first learned of the request for schooners to engage in the business of supplying the factories with Magdalen Island herring at the Customs House in Canso on arrival with the cargo of empty barrels. Word had reached Canso by telegram, for broadcasting through the medium of Custom Offices, and waterfront merchants having contact with trading vessels. The head office for the large lobster-packing factories was at Pictou, in the lower Gulf of St. Lawrence, and the offer quoted the possibility of taking a cargo of supplies and building material from Pictou to Magdalen. This would provide a load each way and increase the gross earnings considerably.

Captain Abe hired extra help and had his cargo of empty barrels discharged in record time. The boat lumber and potatoes brought a good price and was sold practically on arrival. When the last barrel went ashore, sails were hoisted and the *Western Belle* was underway, heading up shore toward Queensport. It was Abe's hope of catching the *Lucy B.* and passing the word along to his rival friend, Mose. Sure enough, two hours later, a few miles south of Queensport, the *Lucy* was sighted coming out from behind the high hills that sheltered the harbour of Queensport.

119

By force of habit, and the urge to exchange a greeting or sarcastic remark, each skipper steered to meet the other. As they approached to within a distance of one mile, Abe brought the *Western Belle* up in the wind and ordered the jibs to be lowered. This was a signal for Captain Mose to heave the *Lucy B.* to also, put a boat out and come on board. Lowering the jibs indicated a conference was the order of the day, and less than twenty minutes later, Captain Mose Griffin was rowed alongside the *Western Belle* in the schooner's lifeboat.

The two schooners jogged head up the bay on the port tack, with a fresh SW breeze, while the two skippers spent at least a good half-hour in conference below in Abe's cabin. It was the first time for the day, and a good reason why each should have a couple of snorts from the little brown jug. Both agreed that there was a big demand out on the south coast for trade and they could have the choice of good charters. But it must have been the yearning for new adventure that made them agree that it would be Pictou for general cargo to Magdalen Islands and a return cargo of fresh herring for some lobster factory.

Ten miles to the NNE lay the south entrance to the Gut of Canso, seventeen miles of a narrow, tide-ridden strait sometimes difficult to navigate, but with a southwest wind it could be sailed through on a northerly passage without tacking. At times the current was so strong that an ordinary sailing vessel could not make headway against it unless with a very strong breeze. However, that was the chance one took when traversing the Straits.

As Mose was leaving the *Western Belle,* her jibs were hoisted and the course set for Cape Argos and the south entrance of the Gut. By the time Captain Mose had rowed alongside his own vessel and got the life-boat hoisted on deck, Abe had a good two miles head start. This he needed because *Lucy* was quite capable of reducing that lead in the next six hours. Abe had figured that out when he used the tactic of causing Mose to put the rowboat in the water.

Slow progress was made for the first two hours in the Strait with the current running south at about two knots, but the tide was due to slack and set northward in a couple of hours. *Lucy B.* was close alongside the *Western Belle* long before the current began to set northward and, for some unknown reason, they remained close for the entire passage through. Off the north light, where the Strait ends and opens out in the lower section of the Gulf of St. Lawrence, the wind was much lighter and veered from a more southerly direction with rain showers. There were several patches of drift ice, chunks about the size of an average two-story dwelling drifting about, and almost all submerged. Here and there a family of seals would be seen playing on the surface, heading northward. There would be at least one adult seal and several smaller ones splashing and plunging through the water.

Cape George is the very high, prominent point of land at just about the most northeasterly part of Nova Scotia. Although twenty-five miles away, it appeared to be "just over there!" After sailing on the south coast of Nova Scotia where the land seldom if ever is higher than one hundred and eighty feet, to see land six and eight hundred feet in height, as is Cape George, gives one a false sense of distance.

The light was glowing that evening in the tall lighthouse tower long before the two schooners rounded the Cape to head up for Pictou Harbour, thirty-six miles WSW from Cape George. In these waters the current runs at a rate of one point five to two knots — quite different from out on the south coast. Fortunately the current was setting westward as they rounded the Cape. The moderate southerly wind was little help but six hours of two knot current was an advantage, so that by daylight the two schooners were moving along at a slow three miles an hour up the long narrow Pictou Harbour. Noon saw both secured alongside the head of the long town wharf. Both captains went to the office of Eastern Packers Ltd. where they bargained to carry general stores to any port in the Magdalen Islands. Once there, they would reload with fresh herring and deliver them to the coastal lobster factories of the Northumberland Strait.

Their cargoes consisted of building material, food stuffs, hay, oats, fishing nets, fish lines and hooks. Loading commenced soon after the skippers arrived at the packers' office and agreed on the charter for the return voyage. The first cargo to go on board was four tons each of fishery salt, required for preserving the bulk cargo of herring during the voyage from the Islands to the mainland, a distance of approximately one hundred and twenty-five miles. For both skippers it was the first time either had been in Pictou and on leaving the packers' office, they decided they should walk around and size up the very pretty old town. It is built on the side of a slope rising from the estuary of two fair-sized rivers, with very fertile soil that produces farm products and timber in quality and abundance. They walked to the highest elevation from where could be seen part of the Northumberland Strait and some of the Gulf of St. Lawrence waters, and a coastline forest of beautiful spruce and birch. Across the harbour, Pictou Landing showed a cleared green slope with whitewashed farm houses and barns.

As they approached the waterfront again, returning to their schooners, the route brought them across a green square or park with benches and well-trimmed trees that shaded the grounds. Here they noticed a monument built from rough granite stones and bearing a plaque which read:

"To commemorate the sailing of the 'SS Royal William'. Built in Quebec, Canada. Sailed from Pictou, Nova Scotia for London, England, 18 August, 1833 and was the first ship to cross the Atlantic from west to east all the way under steam."

The only other ships in the harbour were two large, four-masted, fore-and-aft coastal sailing schooners, one from the Bay of Fundy and the other from Liverpool, Nova Scotia, both loading logs for United States ports. Having had little sleep the night before, both captains agreed to turn in early and get caught up on their rest with the hope of sailing the next evening. The berthing arrangement was so that on arriving at the pier, they came to the *Lucy B.* first, which automatically made Captain Mose the host for the appetizers, and so his favourite brand of "Three H's" was the order of the day.

Abe could enjoy the drink very well, but could not develop just the same taste or desire he had for the Old Demerara, and always teased Mose with his idea that rum was the typical Nova Scotia drink and reckoned to be the right tonic for our climate.

When Captain Abe climbed on the pier from the *Lucy B.* returning to his own schooner, he came face to face with one of the finest teams of oxen he had ever seen. A pair of yoked oxen was dragging a sled affair down the muddy roadway toward the wharf. They pulled a dead weight load estimated at two tons of merchandise to be loaded aboard the schooners.

In the absence of the captains, the mates hired additional help to speed up loading. This move was met with whole-hearted approval by the masters and contributed a lot to being ready to sail next day. A very low spring tide that afternoon caused the mud flats to be dried out and this contaminated the waterfront atmosphere with a flat and muddy odor. It got below in the cabins and forecastles of the vessels and it was not until the flood tide came in and covered

122

the flats that the fresh, clear air returned to the harbour front. The north breeze, coming in off the ice-cold water of Northumberland Strait, chilled the air. The sky was clear and a red sunset back in the west indicated fine weather for the next twenty-four hours at least.

Millwood Jack was a very reserved man with little sense of humor, but occasionally he did break and come up with a dry remark or an act that carried off the show. Having finished eating his supper first, he departed from the forecastle where the other four were eating and discussing the pros and cons of Pictou town. The narrow, tube-like companionway entrance to the forecastle served to amplify Jack's voice as it carried the message from on deck to Captain Abe.

"A girl on the wharf to see you, Skipper!" announced Jack, focussing on eyes across the forecastle table. Abe braced himself, saw the glances of the others and noted sly grins wrinkling the corners of their eyes. He was about to ask for a repeat of the announcement when his ears picked up what appeared, in all seriousness, to be a conversation between someone up on the wharf and Jack. What he heard, and the cunning Jack made sure he would hear, was:

"Yes, lady! I told him you was here."

Publicover could not resist. He spoke first and his remark was:

"Quick work, old man! Quick work me backstays!"

"I knows no woman in this town," came back Abe, but in the same moment he was reaching for the companionway ladder and was on his way up. Jack must have been down at the cabin stove, because when Abe reached the deck there was no cook in sight. Abe glanced up on the wharf and there stood a half-frozen squaw, with a large bundle of beautiful handmade baskets.

"Ump der, Captain, you buy da wif some good basket, ug?"

Jack had caught the old man off guard and left him struggling with his wits to handle the situation. He could hear the snickering of his shipmates where they were crouched in the companionway enjoying the show. Finally Abe broke the silence and advised the squaw to get back to the woods and her wigwam before she froze to death.

"Squaw no freeze. Squaw hungry, Captain, havum no dinner."

Abe knew that statement could be gospel truth and bellowed an order for Jack to come out on deck. Jack's head popped up from the cabin companionway, where it never had been lower than just out of sight.

"You want sumpin, Captain?" replied Jack.

"Yes, flat-foot! Make haste now and get your cousin a good bundle of grub."

"Not my cousin, Skipper," quipped the cook.

"Have me doubts," snapped Abe.

By this time the lady with the baskets had squatted herself on the edge of the wharf, had unstrung several, and was passing them down to Abe telling him to "buy wif some basket". Indian handmade baskets are outstanding in design and workmanship, and appeal to any person with an eye for art and handcraft. The other crew members were on deck now and examining her work. Abe held up three eight-quart baskets and asked:

"How much money you want?"

The old girl had been trained to sell baskets very young, and knew from experience that captains were obligated to maintain a certain standard of dignity, and ought not to be regarded by their men as cheapskates.

"Two dollar cheap, Captain," was the reply.

While Abe was getting the cash from his money bag, Jack arrived on deck with a bundle wrapped with newspaper and a tin mug of hot tea. Abe dropped a fair amount of silver pieces in a basket, took the cup of hot tea away from Jack, ordered the bundle put in the same basket with the silver coins and passed it up to the squaw. He returned the tin mug to Jack with instructions that required him to make a trip to the cabin. The other crew members were bargaining for baskets. As fleet-footed Jack trotted aft to the cabin, a miniature cloud of steam floated under the wharf as the contents of the mug were disposed of before the cook descended to the cabin. There was no delay in his returning on deck, this time having the mug carefully grasped in one hand, with the handle free to be passed to the guest, and a large plug of pipe tobacco in the other hand. In this manner he ascended the main rigging sheer-pole (just below the first ratline) and passed the contents of both hands to the squaw. The piece of tobacco was tucked away in the bosom of her dress, and the contents of the tin mug went gurgling down to where it served best and quickest to warm and liven up every nerve and limb in her body. The cash returns from a half-dozen good sales were knotted in the corner of a large red handkerchief and put in the bosom with the tobacco. Without the least sign of effort she sprang to her feet, swung the string of baskets in circles over her head, and giving a few steps of a traditional dance, interspersed with cries of "Whoopee!" she then went on her way up town. She would make her way to the outskirts of town where the Indian camp was located and a goodly supply of choice basket-making wood was available.

Like Mountains out of the Sea   Chapter 17

By four o'clock Thursday afternoon all cargo space below decks of each schooner had been filled to the hatches. The cargo was heavy and both vessels were deep in the water. A messenger came for the captains to report to the Eastern Packers offices for final orders before sailing.

The cargo on board *Lucy B.* was billed to merchants at Grindstone Island and House Harbour, and the *Western Belle's* cargo billed to Entry Island and Amherst Island. They could pick up herring from any of the fish traps or nets they wished, and agents on the Island would pay for the fish and assist in any way necessary in getting cargos as soon as possible.

The clerk at the packing company attended to business in every detail, even to clearing the schooners through Customs, so that when the charter was signed they were ready to proceed to sea. The first schooner loaded with herring was to sail immediately and deliver her cargo to the Wallace Harbour factory, and the next delivery was to be made to the Pugwash factories, each about fifty miles up the Northumberland Strait on the Nova Scotian north shore.

At six p.m. the fresh northwest breeze carried the two vessels out past the sand spit on the port entrance to Pictou Harbour. Everything on deck had to be well secured as there were times here that the decks were continually awash, sailing through confused waters where wind and tide oppose each other and create choppy and dangerous conditions. Pictou Island lay nine miles off shore — four miles of low flat fertile soil, practically in the centre of the eastern entrance to Northumberland Strait. Until the two schooners had sailed out past this point, it was dangerous to be on deck. The wheelman had a sturdy piece of rope fashioned into a neat-fitting bowline over his waist and shoulder and secured to a ringbolt in the deck. It was quite common for the rush of water past the wheel box to carry the wheelman's feet clear off deck, so it was the use of the rope bowline and his strong grasp of the steering wheel that prevented him from being washed about the deck or possibly out over the bulwark, and overboard. However, once out in the more open water, the swells became longer from crest to crest, and the schooner would ride them easier and drier. All that night they sailed under the lee of the eastern coast of Prince Edward Island, from Cape Bear, north and east to Eastern Point. On departure from Eastern Point by daylight Friday morning, the wind was from a westerly direction and they could steer NNE with free sheet, and point for Entry Island fifty-two miles away, hoping to be secure in the first ports of destination at the Magdalen group before dark.

Many seasoned old seamen agree that there is a special fascination in sighting and approaching isolated islands out on the ocean. They are there over the horizon, like another world altogether, and, as you sail toward them, watching them rise out of the ocean, they appear to come to welcome and shelter you. There's that special something you experience and never forget. Entry Island, the most south-easterly of the Magdalen group, is almost six hundred feet high and can be sighted from the deck of a small schooner on a fine, clear day at least thirty miles away. Amherst Island, Grindstone, Cape Alright and Old Harry are other high peaks that stand out of the sea, and make up the hundred and forty mile coastline perimeter that encircles the group.

When the watches changed at 10.00 a.m. Friday morning, both schooners were well out in the Gulf, the *Lucy B.* leading by at least seven miles, and logging off a good eight knots. The long, low, red cliffs of Prince Edward Island's coastline had gone down over the southern horizon. The Island is over one hundred miles long from NW to SE but in no place does it rise much more than eighty feet above sea level. The wind was veering from west to west-south-west with a clear but hazy atmosphere. However, from the deck of *Western Belle,* both Entry Island and Amherst Islands were up over the northern horizon. The cumulus cloud patch hanging over the land was probably the first indication to an experienced seaman that the group of islands lay in that area, long before the land actually was sighted. Entry Island from this distance appeared like the top half section of a crystal ball.

The slopes that drop down from an elevation of five hundred feet are rounded, bold and steep. A beach on the southwest shore

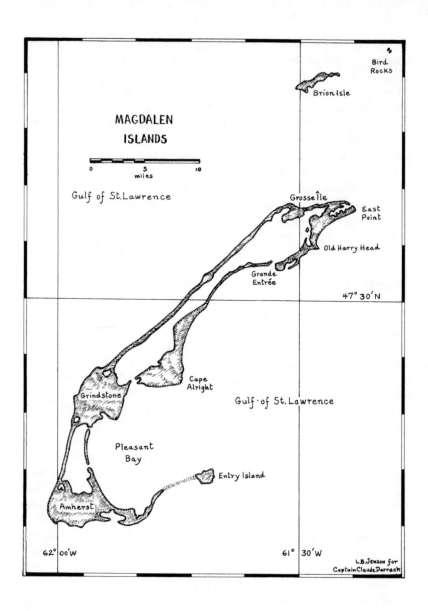

MAGDALEN
ISLANDS

0   5   10
miles

Gulf of St.Lawrence

Bird
Rocks

Brion Isle

Grosse Île

East
Point

Old Harry Head

Grande
Entrée

47° 30′ N

Cape
Alright

Gulf · of St. Lawrence

Grindstone

Pleasant
Bay

Entry Island

Amherst

62° 00′ W

61° 30′ W

L.B. Jenson for
Captain Claude Darrach

128

provides a landing for fishermen, and almost six miles westward rises Amherst Island, its formation resembling a squeezed-in pyramid that points sharply up to a peak four hundred and seventy-seven feet above sea level. The coastline here is very different and spreads out east and north with long sand beaches and bars. Immediately at the east slope is the large lagoon that can be entered through a crooked channel and provides a sheltered harbour which could accommodate at least forty small schooners, providing they didn't require a depth of more than twelve feet of water. At least half the shoreline of Amherst Lagoon is thickly settled with dwellings, fish houses, large smoke-houses and the buildings of half a dozen merchants. The population is made up of English and French-speaking people whose ancestors came from the Channel Islands off the coast of France. Both French and English languages are spoken and understood by young and old, and honesty and good fellowship prevail over the entire group.

By noon the *Lucy B.*, not more than eight miles ahead of the *Western Belle*, appeared suddenly to be transformed from a lofty sailing vessel to a minature toy as she passed close under the bluff east shore of Entry. The proud peaks of her white sails had given way to the wind-swept and ice-carved cliffs as she trimmed sheets, to round the NE coast of Entry, and proceed into Pleasant Bay, nine miles farther on. She would be berthing at a long, well-constructed stone-and-piling wharf to commence discharging the welcome supply of stores she carried.

Skipper Abe was faced with a slightly different problem. It was for him to get the *Western Belle* to the beach head on the southwest side of Entry. This he could do by two different routes: one by carrying on as the *Lucy* had done, around the Island and following the Pleasant Bay shoreline in a southwest direction, or secondly, attempting a narrow channel, thus approaching the Island from the SW, saving at least six miles sailing. But not having local knowledge of the channel and without a chart or aid to navigation, he was finding it hard to make up his mind. All hands were on deck and ready for any event that might arise.

If Abe wanted to save this six miles' unnecessary sailing, the time had come to decide. They had reached a point so close to the Island that it was one thing or the other, and it turned out to be the channel. The skipper ordered the schooner pointed in the wind and the outer jib lowered. When the jib was neatly tied up on the bowsprit, he ordered the port anchor dropped to the water and ten

129

fathoms of chain cable freed to run out on short notice. When Mate Publicover reported to the skipper that the anchor was ready, *Western Belle* was within one mile of the entrance to the channel and in a windward position to proceed in with free sheet. This time the captain relieved the man at the wheel, pointed the vessel into the wind again and ordered the mainsail lowered and furled. Before the large sail was securely rolled and snugly tied between the boom and gaff, Skipper Abe was pleased to see a small rowboat coming out from the beach and heading in their direction. When the boat reached a point midway between the beach and the schooner it stopped and a man was seen waving something.

Abe understood this to mean that the boat was marking the channel entrance and he steered the *Western Belle* toward the boat. Now under the foresail and jumbo, the heavy-laden hull wallowed along at about four knots, slowly but with lots of momentum, having a dead weight displacement of approximately one hundred and eighty tons. They sailed close enough to the rowboat to allow the men to reach out and catch a rope, and be hauled alongside. Abe requested one of the men to come and show him the direction of the channel.

"Keep all the bush to port, Captain," was the instant reply.

This was all the information Captain Abe required, because bobbing here and there ahead of the vessel could be seen spruce treetops, as though they were growing up from the ocean floor. He was also pleased to learn from the pilot that the wharf ahead was in good condition and had sufficient depth of water to bring the schooner alongside. It was time now to lower the foresail and jumbo. An estimated one-half knot current was settling out from Pleasant Bay through the channel that would help to take the headway off, once the sails were lowered. When they were within one hundred yards of the wharf, Abe ordered the anchor dropped. It hadn't gone more than twenty-five feet below the keel when it struck bottom. About seventy feet of slack chain-cable followed out quickly behind the anchor, until the turns around the windlass barrel became taut and stopped it from running. The head movement of the schooner soon stretched out the chain and commenced dragging the anchor over the hard red clay bottom. This action caused the anchor flukes to dig in and hold on so that it brought the heavy old schooner up and around, and finally to a stop, roughly seventy-five feet off the wharf. The end of a strong rope was taken ashore in the rowboat and in no time at all the

Western Belle was tied up alongside the Entry Island Government Wharf, ready to report to Customs and get permission to start discharging cargo.

Over to the northwest, approximately six miles away and still well under sail, was the trim *Lucy B.*, which in another hour would also be snug alongside the Grindstone Government pier. It was just a few steps across the beach and into the office of a large general store warehouse.

When the brief business of entering, paying harbour and light dues, and being granted permission to discharge freight and proceed to take on a load of herring was all taken care of, Abe hurried back on board. He ordered the hatches opened and found the wharf agent waiting to see the bills of lading and accept delivery of the Entry Island consignment. Both the agent and the pilot were invited to the cabin. The pilot was the first to return on deck. His cheeks were flushed and as he climbed ashore it was quite evident that the hard coal gas fumes, or maybe something else he had come in contact with, gave him cause to clear his throat.

The large white mainsails of Lunenburg saltbank fishermen and Gloucester halibuters could be seen across the bay in the Amherst and Grindestone areas. They were in for fresh bait. Thousands of seagulls were hovering and screeching over the large shoals of herring.

Immediately the ice clears off the shore of the Magdalens in spring, the herring rush into the shallow bays and beaches to spawn. There is no exaggeration in the statement that spawn from the herring is sometimes washed up on the beaches in windrows two and three feet high. Yet sufficient eggs escape and mature to replenish that never-failing enormous run of spring herring to these Islands. Thousands of tons are caught. They are used for ground fish bait, lobster bait, smoked and packed in boxes, and salted and cured in barrels for domestic use. The tons and tons of tiny eggs that are destroyed by storms washing the spawn ashore seem to make no difference.

The work schedule on these Gulf Islands was governed to a great extent by the seasons, in such a manner that work days were long. During the period from April until December, some variety of fish and seals were always in abundance. All through that ice-free season, work began at daylight and ended long after the sun had set. By this token, cargo was being discharged from both schooners until ten o'clock in the evening. Seal-oil torches lighted the wharf and roadway, and kerosene lanterns hung in the warehouse to provide light for the work-crew hired to unload and transfer the cargo across the beach to the warehouse. Horsedrawn, two-wheeled carts were the transportation facilities.

In the winter months, December through to March, when all boats were hauled out on the beaches and secured from winter gales and snow, work was confined to repairing fishing gear; repairing boats; sawing imported hardwood into stove lengths to make up a ready fuel supply; and caring for and attending to cattle, sheep and hogs in sufficient quantity to provide the Island's population with adequate reserves of staple foods. Some vegetables were grown on the Island, but the bulk of the supply came from Prince Edward Island. The women folk were specialists in weaving, and knitting wool rugs, all sorts of clothing, socks, wool frocks and trousers, mittens, and headwear of a special design to protect the face and neck when exposed to the blustery Island's winter gales and snowstorms. But it must not be forgotten that there was also time out for social life, fun and entertainment. Talent was not lacking. Music, song and dancing prevailed during the long winter evenings, when contact with the mainland was cut off for months.

Now, this being the first load of freight to arrive at Entry for the season, except for baiting up several of the large Lunenburg and Gloucester fishing schooners, it was the first contact with the mainland for more than three long months. Captain Abe's conversation and announcements pertaining to the many outstanding current events and world-wide headlines of the winter, were burning up the grapevine circulation system. By the time the cargo consigned to Entry was discharged, Abe found himself entrusted with a mailbag he had gratefully accepted and agreed to deliver to the post office at the first port of call on return to the mainland.

At noon, Saturday, Captain Abe returned on board ship and with him was the warehouse and store manager as his guest. They both carried bundles of home handknit woollen socks, mittens and pullover sweaters that Abe had purchased ashore. Skipper, mate and agent settled down to the business of checking and signing the bills of lading. The host had not overlooked the point that each was served with a goodly portion of the contents from the little brown jug!

At the same time, nine miles across Pleasant Bay, Captain Mose Griffin, assisted by a local pilot, was moving the *Lucy B.* from Grindstone to Havre aux Maisons (House Harbour), a distance of not more than three miles, to where the balance of the cargo would be discharged. It was here that she would take on a load of herring; the trap-nets were taking large catches. Grindstone is the most central and main port of the group, and if the Magdalens have a capital, then it may well be Grindstone. Only once in awhile is it separated from most of the other Islands, and that is when high tides cover the long sand bars and beaches. Except for conditions of this sort, travel from Amherst all the way north to Old Harry can be made overland. Amherst, Grindstone and House Harbour were each French-speaking settlements. On Entry Island, Grand Entry and Grosse Isle, the English language was spoken.

Now Captain Abe would be moving from Entry to Amherst, a distance of only six miles, but it was like moving to a different country altogether. At Amherst the English language would be understood, though seldom if ever spoken. The language was not Captain Abe's main concern. It was the question of taking the schooner into the lagoon through the crooked channel and over a dangerous bar. First he would berth at the wharf outside the lagoon at the foot of that steep peak sometimes called Mademoiselle. This was very much exposed to a NE gale; so much so that vessels often were obliged to get away and go to the lagoon, or sail over under the lee of Cape Alright and House Harbour.

When the crew had finished eating dinner, Abe ordered lines taken in, leaving the vessel free to swing on the anchor. In this manner the schooner pointed up in the south breeze and the main and foresails were hoisted. Then the anchor was weighed, the jibs hoisted, and the schooner moved gracefully along in a WSW direction, through the smooth, sheltered water less than a mile off the six mile long sand bar, lashed with choppy Gulf seas on the other side, not more than one half mile to the south.

The arrival at the Amherst wharf presented no problems. Several horse-drawn carts were brought out on the long wharf and then the work of discharging the cargo began.

Two hours after leaving Entry, the *Western Belle* was berthed alongside the Amherst wharf heading in a northeasterly direction, with her skipper on the shore sizing up the situation. He could count on two reasons why he would not be happy in the lagoon. First was the hazard of getting in and out through the channel that he could see now less than a half-mile to the SE; and second, he knew that with a strong north wind he would be held in there waiting favourable conditions to get out. The danger of lost time was enough. *Western Belle* was staying outside and that was that! His next move was to influence the agent to keep the men working through the night until the cargo was unloaded. This he finally succeeded in doing by hiring some help himself, and, of course, entertaining the agent and the Customs representative in the cosy little cabin. Less than one hundred yards from the wharf was a large shoal of herring lying in not more than thirty feet of water. A patch of deep blue water, three or four hundred feet in diameter, indicated a bank of fish on a sand bed, spawning. The water, for at least a mile out in a fan-shaped area, was a milky greyish white, completely saturated with tiny eggs floating in a milky substance that the male fish extrudes into the sea to fertilize and protect the eggs.

Sunday was respected to the extent that prayers and rest replaced other activities. No fishing was engaged in, regardless of the fact that millions of tons of herring and codfish teemed on the shores of the Islands, and lobsters were exceptionally plentiful also. The church bells echoed from the hills and across the waterfront, as young and old, dressed in Sunday best, crossed beaches, clearings and pathways to worship in the humble and plain church buildings.

That May Monday morning dawned with typical Gulf of St. Lawrence spring weather. There was a clear, cool sky with fresh northwest wind. Not too much to prevent the fishermen from rowing the trap-net boats through the choppy water, but sufficient to make it slow and difficult and to prevent the boats from carrying full loads. A strong dry seine net was skillfully flaked in a seine boat and rowed out from the beach by three men, each rowing two oars; the skipper of the boat, located in the bow, with a long slender pole, poked it down in a vertical direction toward the bottom, sounding for a herring shoal. From high on the hillside and from the masthead of the schooners, the blue shaded patches were quite visible, but in a small boat, low on a choppy surface, they could not be seen so well.

The skipper, however, had been looking from on shore and was pulling in the general direction of a shoal. Finally the boat was rowed directly over the bank of herring, and, when the long pole was forced down through the thick mass of live fish, an order from the skipper to ease down on the oars brought relief to the tired oarsmen. It only took a few minutes of holding the pole in the shoal of fish to get the vibrating feeling of the live herring, moving their tails and fins just sufficiently to keep them in a normal position in the water, but not swimming in any direction. (A good and experienced skipper can estimate the tons of herring in a shoal in this manner.) Now, having found a large quantity, they proceeded to heave the seine in a circle and trap the fish. Accompanying boats laid anchors, moored the trap seine in a circular shape, and swept the bottom web of the seine so as to force the herring to a closely packed mass. In this manner they could lower down large dip-nets suspended on the end of long sturdy poles. These would be pushed through the mass of fish, and strong ropes on the bow would serve to haul them back to the surface and upset the contents into the large trap boats.

While several of these sets were being made close off the beaches all along the Island's bays, both the *Lucy B.* at House Harbour and the *Western Belle* at Amherst, were underway, moving out to an anchorage close to the traps, to be conveniently handy for loading. Extra men from the shore were hired to assist. The four tons of salt was hoisted up and dumped on deck near the hatches, and wood chutes were built from the port and starboard bulwark rail to the hatch coaming. The chutes are arranged with sufficient down-grade from the railing to the hatch, so that the slippery fish run freely down the chute and on into the hold. The fishermen then bring the herring-laden boat alongside the schooner and, with small shovel-like dip nets, transfer the herring from the small boat on board the schooner by throwing them up onto the wide-mouthed chute. A scaler looks over the loaded boat and estimates the quantity of her load in barrels. Should he estimate the load to be fourteen barrels, then that goes. The scaler's word is final and the value of the cargo is established in this manner. As the herring run down the chute and into the large cargo hold, one man attends to the job of shovelling salt in amongst the lot. He, too, from experience, has learned the amount necessary to mix with the

135

moisture of melt, spawn and water to make a brine solution strong enough to prevent spoilage for a period of one week (the time required to load, transport and discharge the cargo at the point of destination).

With a lot of hard work and long hours, a vessel the size of *Western Belle* can be loaded with a three hundred barrel cargo of fish in two days, and be on her way toward the port of consignment. This proved true, because at four p.m. Tuesday, Captain Mose Griffin ordered sails hoisted, anchor weighed, and headed the deep laden *Lucy B.* to the ESE and out from Pleasant Bay. Never in the life of the old schooner was she in such a dirty, grimy mess. Mounds of herring eggs had blown about and were spattered over sails, ropes and decks, and were also carried to the forecastle and cabin on oilskins and boots.

The bulky *Western Belle* would have the largest load and would be loaded about six p.m.; then she too would be underway, heading in a northeasterly direction to depart the bay. And this time, which would be after dark, she would have to take the route north and around Entry Island. It would be dangerous attempting to sail through the narrow channel with such a deep-laden craft without benefit of daylight.

By six p.m. *Lucy B.* was out clear of the bay and had settled down on a S by W course — sheets off, and reaching before a fresh NW breeze that provided sufficient choppy sea to send spray, and sometimes solid green water, across the decks to wash the grimy mess out through the scuppers.

Darkness had shut down when *Western Belle* rounded Entry Island, a good mile off shore, yet the huge mound of clay and stone cast a shadow over the water. This made for a situation where, unless one was familiar with the conditions, it was difficult to judge actual distance.

As he paced fore and aft on the starboard quarterdeck of the *Western Belle*, without any lighthouse, buoy or aid other than seamanship and instinct, he safely navigated the deep-laden schooner out past six miles of sand bar, around the four mile shore of Entry Island to clear open water, and head down on the S by W course for Cape Bear, eighty miles to the south. Once in open water, she too, like the *Lucy B.*, began to wash her decks. She was too heavy laden to pitch and roll freely with the choppy wind swell, so the playful white-caps slopped in over the windward rails, ran fore and aft and finally across the decks, making dozens of little

136

streams pouring out through the scuppers. The NW breeze was a gift from the heavens and would carry them along so that when the sun came up over the lofty Cape Breton cliffs next morning, both schooners would have rounded Cape Bear, Prince Edward Island, and be tacking westward through the Northumberland Strait to head into the ports of Pugwash and Wallace with that vital supply of lobster bait.

The Fall Charters

hapter 18

It was not unusual that a return trip from the Northumberland Strait to the Magdalen Islands for a second load of herring was necessary. However, as soon as the demand for lobster bait phased out, many vessels, particularly the largest and ablest, reverted to carrying coal cargoes from the coal-loading docks on the south and east coast of Cape Breton Island — sailing deeply laden with dirty soft coal brought from Cape Breton and peddled among the many fishing villages and settlements along the south and southeast coast of Nova Scotia. These could also be time-consuming cargoes because ready cash was not always available at a port where a goodly supply of coal might be required. School buildings, churches, lighthouse residences, and the usual general store establishment, were good customers. The average private dwelling or homestead would likely supplement the local fuel supply of hardwood with one or two long tons of coal, depending largely on the individual earnings from the fish catches, or in some cases any money otherwise earned to supplement the housekeeping budget. At some settlements men had the opportunity to get some casual labor in the shipyards or export firms that were found in places like Mahone Bay, Ship Harbour, Sheet Harbour, Lunenburg, the LaHave River, Shelburne and Liverpool. Sometimes a full cargo of coal would be consigned to a merchant in one of these ports. These were nice charters to come by.

Toward the end of August the little vessels were tired and weary and ready for a cleaning up and overhaul. Some would be hauled out on a marine slip, but few were available, and so the old traditional method of "careening" was the practice. "Heaving the vessel down" was the expression — an operation executed by fixing stout tackles to the vessel's mastheads, and bringing it alongside a well constructed jetty; or in some cases, if there was a convenient sand beach, securing the other ends of the tackles to suitable anchors and "careening" the vessel to approximately eighty degrees. This way one entire side of the underwater section from waterline to keel was exposed and could be cleaned of growth, caulked and painted. Any repairs necessary to the gudgeons and pintles of the rudder would be made, and the vessel was put in a good seaworthy condition for the most rugged trips of the season's operation when fall set in with shorter daylight, unsettled weather and stronger winds. When the refit procedure was completed, and a brief holiday afforded the crew members, the schooners, one by one, got underway from their respective home ports and sailed to the coal loading docks of Cape Breton Island — Sydney, Glace Bay, Bras d'Or, Port Morien and Louisbourg.

Cape Breton coal varies considerably in quality and price, so it was not always easy for the captain to decide from where, and what type of coal to load, unless it were a charter cargo consigned to a specific firm or person at one port (which was seldom the case). In the great majority of cases the cargoes would be bought by the captain and paid for at dockside. As mentioned before the captain usually was the owner and business manager of the trading schooner. The decision regarding what he should do in each case was based on knowing whether or not there might be ready cash available in the various settlements where he would attempt to peddle the cargo to individual homes of fishermen and others along the coast.

From the easternmost tip of Cape Canso to the coal docks on the eastern side of Cape Breton was approximately one hundred miles, with a choice of two entirely different routes: one via the outer coast route around Scatari or via the Main-a-Dieu passage; the other route was via the Bras d'Or Lakes. The prevailing weather conditions would be the factor in choosing which route to use. Coal cargoes were deep-laden cargoes. After the cargo hold was filled (as much as the stability and buoyancy of the vessel would permit), cargo would be loaded on deck. Now the worry was to get that deck-load safely back over the one hundred mile route to a mainland port, and this did not always work out. These sailing schooners "lived by the wind". Sometimes there was a bit too much breeze, and down went the lee-rail awash, and overboard went the coal. This was not at all a comfortable situation, because perhaps as much as four to six tons of the cargo would have washed off the port-side, but the starboard side cargo would still be intact, with the result that here you were in choppy, windy water, with a starboard list. Well, leave it to those old windjammer seamen. They had gone through this sort of thing before, and no doubt after a couple of hours, waist-deep in green water across the deck, they would trim cargo and get the vessel on an even keel once again. Being aware of this danger on the outer coast, then, there was the advantage of choosing the more sheltered and smoother waters of the Bras d'Or route. The only exception was when the cargoes were loaded at Louisbourg on the south coast of Cape Breton Island. Here only the outer coastal route was practical.

By the latter part of September the mainland coastal requirements would have been pretty well taken care of. Now the larger and ablest vessels would return to the coal docks again, and load cargoes of the best quality coal for Prince Edward Island: Souris, Georgetown, Summerside or Charlottetown. Sheltered ports in the Northumberland Strait waters were of major importance at this season. The distance from port of departure to port of discharge ranged from one hundred and fifty to one hundred and ninety miles. These were rough voyages and demanded a good hull and stout rigging. Winds in the Gulf of St. Lawrence, after October sets in, are either very light or of moderate gale force. The Strait of Canso is affected by the Gulf. So that particular passage under sail could be expected to be rugged unless there was a fair wind which lasted long enough to make the entire run. However this was their life, and there were no highways, in most cases, so supplies must come by water.

When the coal cargoes were discharged, the cargo holds were washed clean and reloaded with Prince Edward Island produce, the famous potatoes and turnips, again for the southeast coast of Nova Scotia. This was a much better cargo, not so heavy as the deep-loaded coal and also lighter work to handle.

During the fall season with its fewer hours of daylight, and cool, frosty nights, any cargo below deck would be well protected in every respect, but the deck cargo (usually turnips) was exposed. To protect it from severe frost, thick layers of dried eel grass were spread over the top and this would be covered with old sail canvas — a technique of securing a cargo that only the coastal packet crewmen understood. The return trip to the south east Nova Scotia coast was much simpler and easier than the trip from Sydney to Prince Edward Island. Prevailing westerly winds made fair weather runs out of the Gulf and around Cape Canso, much to the advantage of a schooner carrying a deckload of perishable produce.

140

It was also the custom to include an average of twenty-five or more carcasses of fresh-killed hogs with the cargo of vegetables. So you can imagine the sense of satisfaction and security in the many homesteads along the coast after having filled the winter cellar with probably an eight month supply of vegetables, salt pork and beef. The appreciation of all this was humbly shown on Thanksgiving Sunday in the community churches all along the coast. It was a traditional event to decorate the church altar with baskets and containers of vegetables, fish, and homemade jam — a gift from each family to the beloved and respected clergy and their families for the spiritual and social benefits with which their presence provided the community.

The expression, "It's the hope of reward that sweetens labor" is ever to be remembered by the younger school children then living in the isolated villages of the coastline. They would spend late hours of the evening after school working on board the potato vessel, holding and filling bags of turnips and potatoes. When the hatches were placed over the cargo hold to call it a day's work, the captain would see that each child was given his choice of what he could carry in his arms of the large turnips among the deck cargo. These were his personal property to take home carefully, and find a suitable place to store. For days afterward he could treat himself or some special friend to a cross-section slice of that crispy vegetable garnished with a wee shake of table salt. There were no potato chips then!

The value of supplying these commodities and necessities of life to the people of the rockbound coast of Nova Scotia is not to be underestimated. There was no other way essential food and domestic materials could be distributed.

When the potato cargoes had been disposed of around late November, this wrote *finis* to another season of rivalry between Abe Young and Mose Griffin. Captains and crew members returned to their families for a period of time, and there was much to do ashore.

The little schooners, too, would find a winter haven. Secure in a well-protected berth, stripped of all running rigging and canvas, they would ride out the winter gales in the sheltered harbour of a home port. Here they would wait for the winds of spring to fill their sails once more for another season of competition, hard work and good fellowship.

Epilogue

This was an era when people were required to be very versatile. Once ashore, the men would find themselves yoking up a team of oxen and cultivating the home garden plot (of at least four acres) which was a chore to be completed before the soil became frozen. A full year's supply of firewood was chopped from the woodlot and hauled home. There were choice logs to be cut, taken to the mill, sawed in a suitable variety of boards required for general repair, or perhaps to build a new home.

There was no thought given to a realaxed schedule until it was agreed that everything was in order for another year, but there was still time for entertainment. It was not unusual to move the desks in the village schoolroom to one side to enjoy a community dance. The floor would be covered with a few pounds of parawax, arrangements made with a couple of fiddlers with piano and accordion accompaniment. A full course meal would be served and the last waltz played sometime in the wee hours of the morning.

Evening musicals and concerts were often planned. "Eight hand straight" forty fives, a card game, was a popular community event at least one night a week, and it was also a daily event in a conveniently located room at the village grocery store. The traditional prize here was anything from a bucket of lard to a quarter of beef.

It was a way of life that included hard work, but also fun and entertainment, which young and old enjoyed together. And the trading schooners, skippered by men like Abe Young and Mose Griffin, were the lifeline of these coastal settlements before the highways, as we know them today, existed.

Thank God for those days and bless the people that made them worthwhile.